Oscar Fingal O'Flahertie Wills Wilde (16 October 1854 – 30 November 1900) was an Irish poet and playwright. After writing in different forms throughout the 1880s, he became one of London's most popular playwrights in the early 1890s. He is best remembered for his epigrams and plays, his novel The Picture of Dorian Gray, and the circumstances of his criminal conviction for homosexuality, imprisonment, and early death at age 46. Wilde's parents were successful Anglo-Irish intellectuals in Dublin. Their son became fluent in French and German early in life. At university, Wilde read Greats; he proved himself to be an outstanding classicist, first at Trinity College Dublin, then at Oxford. He became known for his involvement in the rising philosophy of aestheticism, led by two of his tutors, Walter Pater and John Ruskin. After university, Wilde moved to London into fashionable cultural and social circles. (Source: Wikipedia)

Literary works:
Ravenna (1878)
Poems (1881)
The Happy Prince and Other Stories (1888)
Lord Arthur Savile's Crime and Other Stories (1891)
A House of Pomegranates (1891)
Intentions (1891)
The Picture of Dorian Gray (1890)
The Soul of Man under Socialism (1891)
Lady Windermere's Fan (1892)
A Woman of No Importance (1893)
An Ideal Husband (1898)
The Importance of Being Earnest (1898)
De Profundis (1905)
The Ballad of Reading Gaol (1898)
The Portrait of Mr. W. H. (1889)

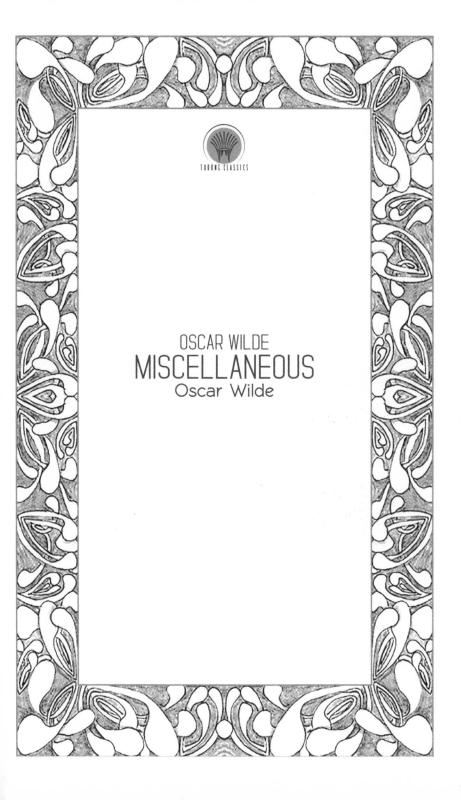

TUDUR CLASSICS

OSCAR WILDE
MISCELLANEOUS
Oscar Wilde

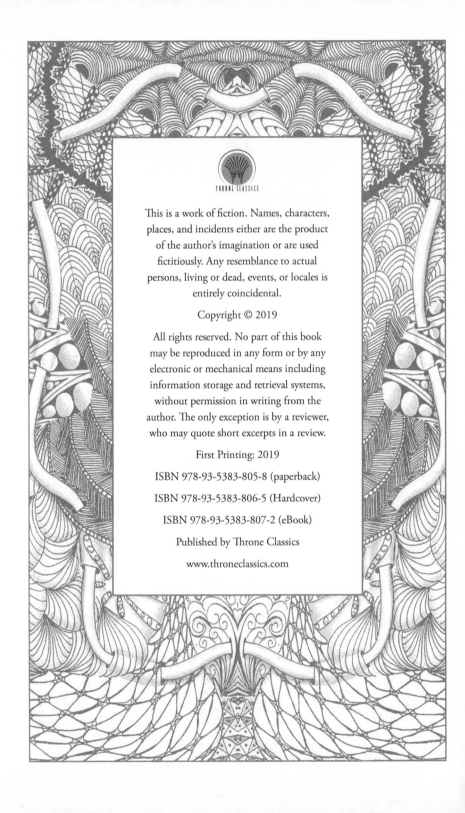

THRONE CLASSICS

Copyright © 2019

First Printing: 2019

ISBN 978-93-5383-805-8 (paperback)

ISBN 978-93-5383-806-5 (Hardcover)

ISBN 978-93-5383-807-2 (eBook)

Published by Throne Classics

www.throneclassics.com

Contents

OSCAR WILDE

MISCELLANEOUS

PREFACE

'As to my personal attitude towards criticism, I confess in brief the following:—"If my works are good and of any importance whatever for the further development of art, they will maintain their place in spite of all adverse criticism and in spite of all hateful suspicions attached to my artistic intentions. If my works are of no account, the most gratifying success of the moment and the most enthusiastic approval of as augurs cannot make them endure. The waste-paper press can devour them as it has devoured many others, and I will not shed a tear . . . and the world will move on just the same."'—RICHARD STRAUSS.

The contents of this volume require some explanation of an historical nature. It is scarcely realised by the present generation that Wilde's works on their first appearance, with the exception of De Profundis, were met with almost general condemnation and ridicule. The plays on their first production were grudgingly praised because their obvious success could not be ignored; but on their subsequent publication in book form they were violently assailed. That nearly all of them have held the stage is still a source of irritation among certain journalists. Salomé however enjoys a singular career. As every one knows, it was prohibited by the Censor when in rehearsal by Madame Bernhardt at the Palace Theatre in 1892. On its publication in 1893 it was greeted with greater abuse than any other of Wilde's works, and was consigned to the usual irrevocable oblivion. The accuracy of the French was freely canvassed, and of course it is obvious that the French is not that of a Frenchman. The play was passed for press, however, by no less a writer than Marcel Schwob whose letter to the Paris publisher, returning the proofs and mentioning two or three slight alterations, is still in my possession. Marcel Schwob told me some years afterwards that he thought it would have spoiled the spontaneity and character of Wilde's style if he had tried to harmonise it with the diction demanded by the French Academy. It was never composed with any idea of presentation. Madame Bernhardt happened to say she wished Wilde would write a play for her; he replied in jest that he had done so. She insisted on seeing the manuscript, and decided on its immediate production, ignorant or forgetful of the English law which prohibits the introduction of Scriptural characters on the stage. With his keen sense of the theatre Wilde would never have contrived the long speech of Salomé at the end in a drama intended for the stage, even in the days of long speeches. His threat to change his nationality shortly after the Censor's interference called forth a most delightful and good-natured caricature of him by Mr. Bernard Partridge in Punch.

Wilde was still in prison in 1896 when Salomé was produced by Lugne Poë at the Théâtre de L'Œuvre in Paris, but except for an account in the Daily Telegraph the incident was hardly mentioned in England. I gather that the performance was only a qualified success, though Lugne Poë's triumph as Herod was generally acknowledged. In 1901, within a year of the author's death, it was produced in Berlin; from that moment it has held the European stage. It has run for a longer consecutive period in Germany than any play by any Englishman, not excepting Shakespeare. Its popularity has extended to all countries where it is not prohibited. It is performed throughout Europe, Asia and America. It is played even in Yiddish. This is remarkable in view of the many dramas by French and German writers who treat of the same theme. To none of them, however, is Wilde indebted. Flaubert, Maeterlinck (some would add Ollendorff) and Scripture, are the obvious sources on which he has freely drawn for what I do not hesitate to call the most powerful and perfect of all his dramas. But on such a point a trustee and executor may be prejudiced because it is the most valuable asset in Wilde's literary estate. Aubrey Beardsley's illustrations are too well known to need more than a passing reference. In the world of art criticism they excited almost as much attention as Wilde's drama has excited in the world of intellect.

During May 1905 the play was produced in England for the first time at a private performance by the New Stage Club. No one present will have forgotten the extraordinary tension of the audience on that occasion, those who disliked the play and its author being hypnotised by the extraordinary power of Mr. Robert Farquharson's Herod, one of the finest pieces of acting ever seen in this country. My friends the dramatic critics (and many of them are personal friends) fell on Salomé with all the vigour of their predecessors twelve years before. Unaware of what was taking place in Germany, they spoke of the play as having been 'dragged from obscurity.' The Official Receiver in Bankruptcy and myself were, however, better informed. And much pleasure has been derived from reading those criticisms, all carefully preserved along with the list of receipts which were simultaneously pouring in from the German performances. To do the critics justice they never withdrew any of their printed opinions, which were all trotted out again when the play was produced privately for the second time in England by the Literary Theatre Society in 1906. In the Speaker of July 14th, 1906, however, some of the iterated misrepresentations of fact were corrected. No attempt was made to controvert the opinion of an ignorant critic: his veracity only was impugned. The powers of vatication possessed by such judges of drama can be fairly tested in the career of Salomé on the European stage, apart from the opera. In an introduction to the English translation published by Mr. John Lane it is pointed out that Wilde's confusion of Herod Antipas (Matt. xiv. 1) with Herod the Great (Matt. ii. 1) and Herod Agrippa I. (Acts xii. 23) is intentional, and follows a mediæval convention. There is no attempt at historical accuracy or archæological exactness. Those who saw the marvellous décor of Mr. Charles Ricketts at the second English production can form a complete idea of what Wilde intended in that respect; although the stage management was clumsy and amateurish. The great opera of Richard Strauss does not fall within my province; but the fag ends of its popularity on the Continent have been imported here oddly enough through the agency of the Palace Theatre, where Salomé was originally to have been performed. Of a young lady's dancing, or of that of her rivals, I am not qualified to speak. I note merely that the critics who objected to the horror of one incident in the drama lost all self-control on seeing that incident repeated in dumb show and accompanied by fescennine corybantics. Except in 'name and borrowed notoriety' the music-hall sensation has no relation whatever to the drama which so profoundly moved the whole of Europe and the greatest living musician. The adjectives of contumely are easily transmuted into epithets of adulation, when a prominent ecclesiastic succumbs, like King Herod, to the fascination of a dancer.

It is not usually known in England that a young French naval officer, unaware that Dr. Strauss was composing an opera on the theme of Salomé, wrote another music drama to accompany Wilde's text. The exclusive musical rights having been already secured by Dr. Strauss, Lieutenant Marriotte's work cannot be performed regularly. One presentation, however, was permitted at Lyons, the composer's native town, where I am told it made an extraordinary impression. In order to give English readers some faint idea of the world-wide effect of Wilde's drama, my friend Mr. Walter Ledger has prepared a short bibliography of certain English and Continental translations.

At the time of Wilde's trial the nearly completed MS. of La Sainte Courtisane was entrusted to Mrs. Leverson, the well-known novelist, who in 1897 went to Paris on purpose to restore it to the author. Wilde immediately left the only copy in a cab. A few days later he laughingly informed me of the loss, and added that a cab was a very proper place for it. I have explained elsewhere that he looked on his works with disdain in his last years, though he was always full of schemes for writing others. All my attempts to recover the lost work failed. The passages here reprinted are from some odd leaves of a first draft. The play is, of course, not unlike Salomé, though it was written in English. It expanded Wilde's favourite theory that when you convert some one to an idea, you lose your faith in it; the same motive runs through Mr. W. H. Honorius the hermit, so far as I recollect the story, falls in love with the courtesan who has come to tempt him, and he reveals to her the secret of the love of God. She immediately becomes a Christian, and is murdered by robbers. Honorius the hermit goes back to Alexandria to pursue a life of pleasure. Two other similar plays Wilde invented in prison, Ahab and Isabel and Pharaoh; he would never write them down, though often importuned to do so. Pharaoh was intensely dramatic and perhaps more original than any of the group. None of these works must be confused with the manuscripts stolen from 16 Tite Street in 1895—namely, the enlarged version of Mr. W. H., the second draft of A Florentine Tragedy, and The Duchess of Padua (which, existing in a prompt copy, was of less importance than the others); nor with The Cardinal of Arragon, the manuscript of which I never saw. I scarcely think it ever existed, though Wilde used to recite proposed passages for it.

Some years after Wilde's death I was looking over the papers and letters rescued from Tite Street when I came across loose sheets of manuscript and typewriting, which I imagined were fragments of The Duchess of Padua; on putting them together in a coherent form I recognised that they belonged to the lost Florentine Tragedy. I assumed that the opening scene, though once extant, had disappeared. One day, however, Mr. Willard wrote that he possessed a typewritten fragment of a play which Wilde had submitted to him, and this he kindly forwarded for my inspection. It agreed in nearly every particular with what I had taken so much trouble to put together. This suggests that the opening scene had never been written, as Mr. Willard's version began where mine did. It was characteristic of the author to finish what he never began.

When the Literary Theatre Society produced Salomé in 1906 they asked me for some other short drama by Wilde to present at the same time, as Salomé does not take very long to play. I offered them the fragment of A Florentine Tragedy. By a fortunate coincidence the poet and dramatist, Mr. Thomas Sturge Moore, happened to be on the committee of this Society, and to him was entrusted the task of writing an opening scene to make the play complete. It is not for me to criticise his work, but there is justification for saying that Wilde himself would have envied, with an artist's envy, such lines as—

We will sup with the moon,

Like Persian princes that in Babylon

Sup in the hanging gardens of the King.

In a stylistic sense Mr. Sturge Moore accomplished a feat in reconstruction, whatever opinions may be held of A Florentine Tragedy by Wilde's admirers or detractors. The achievement is particularly remarkable because Mr. Sturge Moore has nothing in common with Wilde other than what is shared by all real poets and dramatists: He is a landed proprietor on Parnassus, not a trespasser. In England we are more familiar with the poachers. Time and Death are of course necessary before there can come any adequate recognition of one of our most original and gifted singers.

Among his works are The Vinedresser and other Poems (1899), Absalom, A Chronicle Play (1903), and The Centaur's Booty (1903). Mr. Sturge Moore is also an art critic of distinction, and his learned works on Dürer (1905) and Correggio (1906) are more widely known (I am sorry to say) than his powerful and enthralling poems.

Once again I must express my obligations to Mr. Stuart Mason for revising and correcting the proofs of this new edition.

ROBERT ROSS

LA SAINTE COURTISANE

A FRAGMENT

LA SAINTE COURTISANE

OR, THE WOMAN COVERED WITH JEWELS

The scene represents the corner of a valley in the Thebaid. On the right hand of the stage is a cavern. In front of the cavern stands a great crucifix.

On the left [sand dunes].

The sky is blue like the inside of a cup of lapis lazuli. The hills are of red sand. Here and there on the hills there are clumps of thorns.

First Man. Who is she? She makes me afraid. She has a purple cloak and her hair is like threads of gold. I think she must be the daughter of the Emperor. I have heard the boatmen say that the Emperor has a daughter who wears a cloak of purple.

Second Man. She has birds' wings upon her sandals, and her tunic is of the colour of green corn. It is like corn in spring when she stands still. It is like young corn troubled by the shadows of hawks when she moves. The pearls on her tunic are like many moons.

First Man. They are like the moons one sees in the water when the wind blows from the hills.

Second Man. I think she is one of the gods. I think she comes from Nubia.

First Man. I am sure she is the daughter of the Emperor. Her nails are stained with henna. They are like the petals of a rose. She has come here to weep for Adonis.

Second Man. She is one of the gods. I do not know why she has left her temple. The gods should not leave their temples. If she speaks to us let us not answer, and she will pass by.

First Man. She will not speak to us. She is the daughter of the Emperor.

Myrrhina. Dwells he not here, the beautiful young hermit, he who will not look on the face of woman?

First Man. Of a truth it is here the hermit dwells.

Myrrhina. Why will he not look on the face of woman?

Second Man. We do not know.

Myrrhina. Why do ye yourselves not look at me?

First Man. You are covered with bright stones, and you dazzle our eyes.

Second Man. He who looks at the sun becomes blind. You are too bright to look at. It is not wise to look at things that are very bright. Many of the priests in the temples are blind, and have slaves to lead them.

Myrrhina. Where does he dwell, the beautiful young hermit who will not look on the face of woman? Has he a house of reeds or a house of burnt clay or does he lie on the hillside? Or does he make his bed in the rushes?

First Man. He dwells in that cavern yonder.

Myrrhina. What a curious place to dwell in!

First Man. Of old a centaur lived there. When the hermit came the centaur gave a shrill cry, wept and lamented, and galloped away.

Second Man. No. It was a white unicorn who lived in the cave. When it saw the hermit coming the unicorn knelt down and worshipped him. Many people saw it worshipping him.

First Man. I have talked with people who saw it.

· · · · ·

Second Man. Some say he was a hewer of wood and worked for hire. But that may not be true.

16

. . . . .

Myrrhina. What gods then do ye worship? Or do ye worship any gods? There are those who have no gods to worship. The philosophers who wear long beards and brown cloaks have no gods to worship. They wrangle with each other in the porticoes. The [ ] laugh at them.

First Man. We worship seven gods. We may not tell their names. It is a very dangerous thing to tell the names of the gods. No one should ever tell the name of his god. Even the priests who praise the gods all day long, and eat of their food with them, do not call them by their right names.

Myrrhina. Where are these gods ye worship?

First Man. We hide them in the folds of our tunics. We do not show them to any one. If we showed them to any one they might leave us.

Myrrhina. Where did ye meet with them?

First Man. They were given to us by an embalmer of the dead who had found them in a tomb. We served him for seven years.

Myrrhina. The dead are terrible. I am afraid of Death.

First Man. Death is not a god. He is only the servant of the gods.

Myrrhina. He is the only god I am afraid of. Ye have seen many of the gods?

First Man. We have seen many of them. One sees them chiefly at night time. They pass one by very swiftly. Once we saw some of the gods at daybreak. They were walking across a plain.

Myrrhina. Once as I was passing through the market place I heard a sophist from Cilicia say that there is only one God. He said it before many people.

First Man. That cannot be true. We have ourselves seen many, though we are but common men and of no account. When I saw them I hid myself in a bush. They did me no harm.

17

· · · · ·

Myrrhina. Tell me more about the beautiful young hermit. Talk to me about the beautiful young hermit who will not look on the face of woman. What is the story of his days? What mode of life has he?

First Man. We do not understand you.

Myrrhina. What does he do, the beautiful young hermit? Does he sow or reap? Does he plant a garden or catch fish in a net? Does he weave linen on a loom? Does he set his hand to the wooden plough and walk behind the oxen?

Second Man. He being a very holy man does nothing. We are common men and of no account. We toll all day long in the sun. Sometimes the ground is very hard.

Myrrhina. Do the birds of the air feed him? Do the jackals share their booty with him?

First Man. Every evening we bring him food. We do not think that the birds of the air feed him.

Myrrhina. Why do ye feed him? What profit have ye in so doing?

Second Man. He is a very holy man. One of the gods whom he has offended has made him mad. We think he has offended the moon.

Myrrhina. Go and tell him that one who has come from Alexandria desires to speak with him.

First Man. We dare not tell him. This hour he is praying to his God. We pray thee to pardon us for not doing thy bidding.

Myrrhina. Are ye afraid, of him?

First Man. We are afraid of him.

Myrrhina. Why are ye afraid of him?

First Man. We do not know.

18

Myrrhina. What is his name?

First Man. The voice that speaks to him at night time in the cavern calls to him by the name of Honorius. It was also by the name of Honorius that the three lepers who passed by once called to him. We think that his name is Honorius.

Myrrhina. Why did the three lepers call to him?

First Man. That he might heal them.

Myrrhina. Did he heal them?

Second Man. No. They had committed some sin: it was for that reason they were lepers. Their hands and faces were like salt. One of them wore a mask of linen. He was a king's son.

Myrrhina. What is the voice that speaks to him at night time in his cave?

First Man. We do not know whose voice it is. We think it is the voice of his God. For we have seen no man enter his cavern nor any come forth from it.

. . . . .

Myrrhina. Honorius.

Honorius (*from within*). Who calls Honorius?

Myrrhina. Come forth, Honorius.

. . . . .

My chamber is ceiled with cedar and odorous with myrrh. The pillars of my bed are of cedar and the hangings are of purple. My bed is strewn with purple and the steps are of silver. The hangings are sewn with silver pomegranates and the steps that are of silver are strewn with saffron and with myrrh. My lovers hang garlands round the pillars of my house. At night time they come with the flute players and the players of the harp. They woo me with apples and on the pavement of my courtyard they write my name in wine.

From the uttermost parts of the world my lovers come to me. The kings of the earth come to me and bring me presents.

When the Emperor of Byzantium heard of me he left his porphyry chamber and set sail in his galleys. His slaves bare no torches that none might know of his coming. When the King of Cyprus heard of me he sent me ambassadors. The two Kings of Libya who are brothers brought me gifts of amber.

I took the minion of Cæsar from Cæsar and made him my playfellow. He came to me at night in a litter. He was pale as a narcissus, and his body was like honey.

The son of the Præfect slew himself in my honour, and the Tetrarch of Cilicia scourged himself for my pleasure before my slaves.

The King of Hierapolis who is a priest and a robber set carpets for me to walk on.

Sometimes I sit in the circus and the gladiators fight beneath me. Once a Thracian who was my lover was caught in the net. I gave the signal for him to die and the whole theatre applauded. Sometimes I pass through the gymnasium and watch the young men wrestling or in the race. Their bodies are bright with oil and their brows are wreathed with willow sprays and with myrtle. They stamp their feet on the sand when they wrestle and when they run the sand follows them like a little cloud. He at whom I smile leaves his companions and follows me to my home. At other times I go down to the harbour and watch the merchants unloading their vessels. Those that come from Tyre have cloaks of silk and earrings of emerald. Those that come from Massilia have cloaks of fine wool and earrings of brass. When they see me coming they stand on the prows of their ships and call to me, but I do not answer them. I go to the little taverns where the sailors lie all day long drinking black wine and playing with dice and I sit down with them.

I made the Prince my slave, and his slave who was a Tyrian I made my lord for the space of a moon.

I put a figured ring on his finger and brought him to my house. I have wonderful things in my house.

The dust of the desert lies on your hair and your feet are scratched with thorns and your body is scorched by the sun. Come with me, Honorius, and I will clothe you in a tunic of silk. I will smear your body with myrrh and pour spikenard on your hair. I will clothe you in hyacinth and put honey in your mouth. Love—

Honorius. There is no love but the love of God.

Myrrhina. Who is He whose love is greater than that of mortal men?

Honorius. It is He whom thou seest on the cross, Myrrhina. He is the Son of God and was born of a virgin. Three wise men who were kings brought Him offerings, and the shepherds who were lying on the hills were wakened by a great light.

The Sibyls knew of His coming. The groves and the oracles spake of Him. David and the prophets announced Him. There is no love like the love of God nor any love that can be compared to it.

The body is vile, Myrrhina. God will raise thee up with a new body which will not know corruption, and thou shalt dwell in the Courts of the Lord and see Him whose hair is like fine wool and whose feet are of brass.

Myrrhina. The beauty . . .

Honorius. The beauty of the soul increases until it can see God. Therefore, Myrrhina, repent of thy sins. The robber who was crucified beside Him He brought into Paradise.

[*Exit.*

Myrrhina. How strangely he spake to me. And with what scorn did he regard me. I wonder why he spake to me so strangely.

· · · · ·

Honorius. Myrrhina, the scales have fallen from my eyes and I see now clearly what I did not see before. Take me to Alexandria and let me taste of the seven sins.

Myrrhina. Do not mock me, Honorius, nor speak to me with such bitter words. For I have repented of my sins and I am seeking a cavern in this desert where I too may dwell so that my soul may become worthy to see God.

Honorius. The sun is setting, Myrrhina. Come with me to Alexandria.

Myrrhina. I will not go to Alexandria.

Honorius. Farewell, Myrrhina.

Myrrhina. Honorius, farewell. No, no, do not go.

. . . . .

I have cursed my beauty for what it has done, and cursed the wonder of my body for the evil that it has brought upon you.

Lord, this man brought me to Thy feet. He told me of Thy coming upon earth, and of the wonder of Thy birth, and the great wonder of Thy death also. By him, O Lord, Thou wast revealed to me.

Honorius. You talk as a child, Myrrhina, and without knowledge. Loosen your hands. Why didst thou come to this valley in thy beauty?

Myrrhina. The God whom thou worshippest led me here that I might repent of my iniquities and know Him as the Lord.

Honorius. Why didst thou tempt me with words?

Myrrhina. That thou shouldst see Sin in its painted mask and look on Death in its robe of Shame.

A FLORENTINE TRAGEDY

WITH OPENING SCENE BY T. STURGE MOORE

This play is only a fragment and was never completed. For the purposes of presentation, the well-known poet, Mr. T. Sturge Moore, has written an opening scene which is here included. Wilde's work begins with the entrance of Simone.

A private performance was given by the Literary Theatre Club in 1906. The first public presentation was given by the New English Players at the Cripplegate Institute, Golden Lane, E.C., in 1907. German, French and Hungarian translations have been presented on the Continental stage.

Dramatic and literary rights are the property of Robert Ross. The American literary and dramatic rights are vested in John Luce and Co., Boston, U.S.A.

CHARACTERS

GUIDO BARDI, A Florentine prince.

SIMONE, a merchant.

BIANNA, his wife.

MARIA, a tire-woman.

The action takes place at Florence in the early sixteenth century.

A FLORENTINE TRAGEDY

[The scene represents a tapestried upper room giving on to a balcony or loggia in an old house at Florence. A table laid for a frugal meal, a spinning-wheel, distaff, etc., chests, chairs and stools.]

As the Curtain rises enter Bianca, with her Servant, Maria.

Maria. Certain and sure, the sprig is Guido Bardi,

A lovely lord, a lord whose blood is blue!

Bianca. But where did he receive you?

Maria. Where, but there

In yonder palace, in a painted hall!—

Painted with naked women on the walls,—

Would make a common man or blush or smile

But he seemed not to heed them, being a lord.

Bianca. But how know you 'tis not a chamberlayne,

A lackey merely?

Maria. Why, how know I there is a God in heaven?

Because the angels have a master surely.

So to this lord they bowed, all others bowed,

And swept the marble flags, doffing their caps,

With the gay plumes. Because he stiffly said,

And seemed to see me as those folk are seen

That will be never seen again by you,

'Woman, your mistress then returns this purse

Of forty thousand crowns, is it fifty thousand?

Come name the sum will buy me grace of her.'

Bianca. What, were there forty thousand crowns therein?

Maria. I know it was all gold; heavy with gold.

Bianca. It must be he, none else could give so much.

Maria. 'Tis he, 'tis my lord Guido, Guido Bardi.

Bianca. What said you?

Maria. I, I said my mistress never

Looked at the gold, never opened the purse,

Never counted a coin. But asked again

What she had asked before, 'How young you looked?

How handsome your lordship looked? What doublet

Your majesty had on? What chains, what hose

Upon your revered legs?' And curtseyed

I, . . .

Bianca. What said he?

Maria. Curtseyed I, and he replied,

'Has she a lover then beside that old

Soured husband or is it him she loves, my God!

Is it him?'

Bianca. Well?

Maria. Curtseyed I low and said

'Not him, my lord, nor you, nor no man else.

Thou art rich, my lord, and honoured, my lord, and she

Though not so rich is honoured . . .'

Bianca. Fool, you fool,

I never bid you say a word of that.

Maria. Nor did I say a word of that you said;

I said, 'She loves him not, my lord, nor loves

Any man else. Yet she might like to love,

If she were loved by one who pleased her well;

For she is weary of spinning long alone.

She is not rich and yet she is not poor; but young

She is, my lord, and you are young.

[*Pauses smiling.*]

Bianca. Quick, quick!

Maria. There, there! 'Twas but to show you how I smiled

Saying the lord was young. It took him too;

For he said, 'This will do! If I should call

To-night to pay respect unto your lovely—

Our lovely mistress, tell her that I said,

Our lovely mistress, shall I be received?'

And I said, 'Yes.' 'Then say I come and if

All else is well let her throw down some favour

When as I pass below.' He should be there!

Look from the balcony; he should be there!—

And there he is, dost see?

Bianca. Some favour. Yes.

This ribbon weighted by this brooch will do.

Maria, be you busy near within, but, till

I call take care you enter not. Go down

And let the young lord in, for hark, he knocks.

[*Exit* Maria.]

Great ladies might he choose from and yet he

Is drawn . . . ah, there my fear is! Was he drawn

By love to me—by love's young strength alone?

That's where it is, if I were sure he loved,

I then might do what greater dames have done

And venge me on a husband blind to beauty.

But if! Ah if! he is a wandering bee,

Mere gallant taster, who befools poor flowers . . .

[Maria *opens the door for* Guido Bardi, *and then withdraws.*]

My lord, I learn that we have something here,

In this poor house, which thou dost wish to buy.

My husband is from home, but my poor fate

Has made me perfect in the price of velvets,

Of silks and gay brocades. I think you offered

Some forty thousand crowns, or fifty thousand,

For something we have here? And it must be

That wonder of the loom, which my Simone

Has lately home; it is a Lucca damask,

The web is silver over-wrought with roses.

Since you did offer fifty thousand crowns

It must be that. Pray wait, for I will fetch it.

Guido. Nay, nay, thou gracious wonder of a loom

More cunning far than those of Lucca, I

Had in my thought no damask silver cloth

By hunch-back weavers woven toilsomely,

If such are priced at fifty thousand crowns

It shames me, for I hoped to buy a fabric

For which a hundred thousand then were little.

Bianca. A hundred thousand was it that you said?

Nay, poor Simone for so great a sum

Would sell you everything the house contains.

The thought of such a sum doth daze the brains

Of merchant folk who live such lives as ours.

Guido. Would he sell everything this house contains?

And every one, would he sell every one?

Bianca. Oh, everything and every one, my lord,

Unless it were himself; he values not

A woman as a velvet, or a wife

At half the price of silver-threaded woof.

Guido. Then I would strike a bargain with him straight,

Bianca. He is from home; may be will sleep from home;

But I, my lord, can show you all we have;

Can measure ells and sum their price, my lord.

Guido. It is thyself, Bianca, I would buy.

Bianca. O, then, my lord, it must be with Simone

You strike your bargain; for to sell myself

Would be to do what I most truly loathe.

Good-night, my lord; it is with deep regret

I find myself unable to oblige

Your lordship.

Guido. Nay, I pray thee let me stay

And pardon me the sorry part I played,

As though I were a chapman and intent

To lower prices, cheapen honest wares.

Bianca. My lord, there is no reason you should stay.

Guido. Thou art my reason, peerless, perfect, thou,

The reason I am here and my life's goal,

For I was born to love the fairest things . . .

Bianca. To buy the fairest things that can be bought.

Guido. Cruel Bianca! Cover me with scorn,

I answer born to love thy priceless self,

That never to a market could be brought,

No more than winged souls that sail and soar

Among the planets or about the moon.

Bianca. It is so much thy habit to buy love,

Or that which is for sale and labelled love,

Hardly couldst thou conceive a priceless love.

But though my love has never been for sale

I have been in a market bought and sold.

Guido. This is some riddle which thy sweet wit reads

To baffle mine and mock me yet again.

Bianca. My marriage, sir, I speak of marriage now,

That common market where my husband went

And prides himself he made a bargain then.

Guido. The wretched chapman, how I hate his soul.

Bianca. He was a better bidder than thyself,

And knew with whom to deal . . . he did not speak

Of gold to me, but in my father's ear

He made it clink: to me he spoke of love,

Honest and free and open without price.

Guido. O white Bianca, lovely as the moon,

The light of thy pure soul and shining wit

Shows me my shame, and makes the thing I was

Slink like a shadow from the thing I am.

Bianca. Let that which casts the shadow act, my lord,

And waste no thought on what its shadow does

Or has done. Are youth, and strength, and love

Balked by mere shadows, so that they forget

Themselves so far they cannot be recalled?

Guido. Nobility is here, not in the court.

There are the tinsel stars, here is the moon,

Whose tranquil splendour makes a day of night.

I have been starved by ladies, specks of light,

And glory drowns me now I see the moon.

Bianca. I have refused round sums of solid gold

And shall not be by tinsel phrases bought.

Guido. Dispute no more, witty, divine Bianca;

Dispute no more. See I have brought my lute!

Close lock the door. We will sup with the moon

Like Persian princes, that, in Babylon

Sup in the hanging gardens of the king.

I know an air that can suspend the soul

As high in heaven as those towered-gardens hang.

Bianca. My husband may return, we are not safe.

Guido. Didst thou not say that he would sleep from home?

Bianca. He was not sure, he said it might be so.

He was not sure—and he would send my aunt

To sleep with me, if he did so decide,

And she has not yet come.

Guido [*starting*] Hark, what's that?

[*They listen, the sound of* Maria's *voice in anger with some one is faintly heard.*]

Bianca. It is Maria scolds some gossip crone.

Guido. I thought the other voice had been a man's.

Bianca. All still again, old crones are often gruff.

You should be gone, my lord.

Guido. O, sweet Bianca!

How can I leave thee now! Thy beauty made

Two captives of my eyes, and they were mad

To feast them on thy form, but now thy wit,

The liberated perfume of a bud,

Which while a bud seemed perfect, but now is

That which can make its former self forgot:

How can I leave the flower who loved the leaf?

Till now I was the richest prince in Florence,

I am a lover now would shun its throngs,

And put away all state and seek retreat

At Bellosguardo or Fiesole,

Where roses in their fin'st profusion hide

Some marble villa whose cool walls have rung

A laughing echo to Decameron,

And where thy laughter shall as gaily sound.

Say thou canst love or with a silent kiss

Instil that balmy knowledge on my soul.

Bianca. Canst tell me what love is?

Guido. It is consent,

The union of two minds, two souls, two hearts,

In all they think and hope and feel.

Bianca. Such lovers might as well be dumb, for those

Who think and hope and feel alike can never

Have anything for one another's ear.

Guido. Love is? Love is the meeting of two worlds

In never-ending change and counter-change.

Bianca. Thus will my husband praise the mercer's mart,

Where the two worlds of East and West exchange.

Guido. Come. Love is love, a kiss, a close embrace.

It is . . .

Bianca. My husband calls that love

When he hath slammed his weekly ledger to.

Guido. I find my wit no better match for thine

Than thou art match for an old crabbed man;

But I am sure my youth and strength and blood

Keep better tune with beauty gay and bright

As thine is, than lean age and miser toil.

Bianca. Well said, well said, I think he would not dare

To face thee, more than owls dare face the sun;

He's the bent shadow such a form as thine

Might cast upon a dung heap by the road,

Though should it fall upon a proper floor

Twould be at once a better man than he.

Guido. Your merchant living in the dread of loss

Becomes perforce a coward, eats his heart.

Dull souls they are, who, like caged prisoners watch

And envy others' joy; they taste no food

But what its cost is present to their thought.

Bianca. I am my father's daughter, in his eyes

A home-bred girl who has been taught to spin.

He never seems to think I have a face

Which makes you gallants turn where'er I pass.

Guido. Thy night is darker than I dreamed, bright Star.

Bianca. He waits, stands by, and mutters to himself,

And never enters with a frank address

To any company. His eyes meet mine

And with a shudder I am sure he counts

The cost of what I wear.

Guido. Forget him quite.

Come, come, escape from out this dismal life,

As a bright butterfly breaks spider's web,

And nest with me among those rosy bowers,

Where we will love, as though the lives we led

Till yesterday were ghoulish dreams dispersed

By the great dawn of limpid joyous life.

Bianca. Will I not come?

Guido. O, make no question, come.

They waste their time who ponder o'er bad dreams.

We will away to hills, red roses clothe,

And though the persons who did haunt that dream

Live on, they shall by distance dwindled, seem

No bigger than the smallest ear of corn

That cowers at the passing of a bird,

And silent shall they seem, out of ear-shot,

Those voices that could jar, while we gaze back

From rosy caves upon the hill-brow open,

And ask ourselves if what we see is not

A picture merely,—if dusty, dingy lives

Continue there to choke themselves with malice.

Wilt thou not come, Bianca? Wilt thou not?

[*A sound on the stair.*]

guido. What's that?

[*The door opens, they separate guiltily, and the husband enters.*]

Simone. My good wife, you come slowly; were it not better

To run to meet your lord? Here, take my cloak.

Take this pack first. 'Tis heavy. I have sold nothing:

Save a furred robe unto the Cardinal's son,

Who hopes to wear it when his father dies,

And hopes that will be soon.

But who is this?

Why you have here some friend. Some kinsman doubtless,

Newly returned from foreign lands and fallen

Upon a house without a host to greet him?

I crave your pardon, kinsman. For a house

Lacking a host is but an empty thing

And void of honour; a cup without its wine,

A scabbard without steel to keep it straight,

A flowerless garden widowed of the sun.

Again I crave your pardon, my sweet cousin.

Bianca. This is no kinsman and no cousin neither.

Simone. No kinsman, and no cousin! You amaze me.

Who is it then who with such courtly grace

Deigns to accept our hospitalities?

Guido. My name is Guido Bardi.

Simone. What! The son

Of that great Lord of Florence whose dim towers

Like shadows silvered by the wandering moon

I see from out my casement every night!

Sir Guido Bardi, you are welcome here,

Twice welcome. For I trust my honest wife,

Most honest if uncomely to the eye,

Hath not with foolish chatterings wearied you,

As is the wont of women.

Guido. Your gracious lady,

Whose beauty is a lamp that pales the stars

And robs Diana's quiver of her beams

Has welcomed me with such sweet courtesies

That if it be her pleasure, and your own,

I will come often to your simple house.

And when your business bids you walk abroad

I will sit here and charm her loneliness

Lest she might sorrow for you overmuch.

What say you, good Simone?

Simone. My noble Lord,

You bring me such high honour that my tongue

Like a slave's tongue is tied, and cannot say

The word it would. Yet not to give you thanks

Were to be too unmannerly. So, I thank you,

From my heart's core.

It is such things as these

That knit a state together, when a Prince

So nobly born and of such fair address,

Forgetting unjust Fortune's differences,

Comes to an honest burgher's honest home

As a most honest friend.

And yet, my Lord,

I fear I am too bold. Some other night

We trust that you will come here as a friend;

To-night you come to buy my merchandise.

Is it not so? Silks, velvets, what you will,

I doubt not but I have some dainty wares

Will woo your fancy. True, the hour is late,

But we poor merchants toil both night and day

To make our scanty gains. The tolls are high,

And every city levies its own toll,

And prentices are unskilful, and wives even

Lack sense and cunning, though Bianca here

Has brought me a rich customer to-night.

Is it not so, Bianca? But I waste time.

Where is my pack? Where is my pack, I say?

Open it, my good wife. Unloose the cords.

Kneel down upon the floor. You are better so.

Nay not that one, the other. Despatch, despatch!

Buyers will grow impatient oftentimes.

We dare not keep them waiting. Ay! 'tis that,

Give it to me; with care. It is most costly.

Touch it with care. And now, my noble Lord—

Nay, pardon, I have here a Lucca damask,

The very web of silver and the roses

So cunningly wrought that they lack perfume merely

To cheat the wanton sense. Touch it, my Lord.

Is it not soft as water, strong as steel?

And then the roses! Are they not finely woven?

I think the hillsides that best love the rose,

At Bellosguardo or at Fiesole,

Throw no such blossoms on the lap of spring,

Or if they do their blossoms droop and die.

Such is the fate of all the dainty things

That dance in wind and water. Nature herself

Makes war on her own loveliness and slays

Her children like Medea. Nay but, my Lord,

Look closer still. Why in this damask here

It is summer always, and no winter's tooth

Will ever blight these blossoms. For every ell

I paid a piece of gold. Red gold, and good,

The fruit of careful thrift.

Guido. Honest Simone,

Enough, I pray you. I am well content;

To-morrow I will send my servant to you,

Who will pay twice your price.

Simone. My generous Prince!

I kiss your hands. And now I do remember

Another treasure hidden in my house

Which you must see. It is a robe of state:

Woven by a Venetian: the stuff, cut-velvet:

The pattern, pomegranates: each separate seed

Wrought of a pearl: the collar all of pearls,

As thick as moths in summer streets at night,

And whiter than the moons that madmen see
Through prison bars at morning. A male ruby
Burns like a lighted coal within the clasp
The Holy Father has not such a stone,
Nor could the Indies show a brother to it.
The brooch itself is of most curious art,
Cellini never made a fairer thing
To please the great Lorenzo. You must wear it.
There is none worthier in our city here,
And it will suit you well. Upon one side
A slim and horned satyr leaps in gold
To catch some nymph of silver. Upon the other
Stands Silence with a crystal in her hand,
No bigger than the smallest ear of corn,
That wavers at the passing of a bird,
And yet so cunningly wrought that one would say,
It breathed, or held its breath.

Worthy Bianca,
Would not this noble and most costly robe
Suit young Lord Guido well?

Nay, but entreat him;
He will refuse you nothing, though the price
Be as a prince's ransom. And your profit

Shall not be less than mine.

Bianca. Am I your prentice?

Why should I chaffer for your velvet robe?

Guido. Nay, fair Bianca, I will buy the robe,

And all things that the honest merchant has

I will buy also. Princes must be ransomed,

And fortunate are all high lords who fall

Into the white hands of so fair a foe.

Simone. I stand rebuked. But you will buy my wares?

Will you not buy them? Fifty thousand crowns

Would scarce repay me. But you, my Lord, shall have them

For forty thousand. Is that price too high?

Name your own price. I have a curious fancy

To see you in this wonder of the loom

Amidst the noble ladies of the court,

A flower among flowers.

They say, my lord,

These highborn dames do so affect your Grace

That where you go they throng like flies around you,

Each seeking for your favour.

I have heard also

Of husbands that wear horns, and wear them bravely,

A fashion most fantastical.

Guido. Simone,

Your reckless tongue needs curbing; and besides,

You do forget this gracious lady here

Whose delicate ears are surely not attuned

To such coarse music.

Simone. True: I had forgotten,

Nor will offend again. Yet, my sweet Lord,

You'll buy the robe of state. Will you not buy it?

But forty thousand crowns—'tis but a trifle,

To one who is Giovanni Bardi's heir.

Guido. Settle this thing to-morrow with my steward,

Antonio Costa. He will come to you.

And you shall have a hundred thousand crowns

If that will serve your purpose.

Simone. A hundred thousand!

Said you a hundred thousand? Oh! be sure

That will for all time and in everything

Make me your debtor. Ay! from this time forth

My house, with everything my house contains

Is yours, and only yours.

A hundred thousand!

My brain is dazed. I shall be richer far

Than all the other merchants. I will buy

Vineyards and lands and gardens. Every loom

From Milan down to Sicily shall be mine,

And mine the pearls that the Arabian seas

Store in their silent caverns.

Generous Prince,

This night shall prove the herald of my love,

Which is so great that whatsoe'er you ask

It will not be denied you.

Guido. What if I asked

For white Bianca here?

Simone. You jest, my Lord;

She is not worthy of so great a Prince.

She is but made to keep the house and spin.

Is it not so, good wife? It is so. Look!

Your distaff waits for you. Sit down and spin.

Women should not be idle in their homes,

For idle fingers make a thoughtless heart.

Sit down, I say.

Bianca. What shall I spin?

Simone. Oh! spin

Some robe which, dyed in purple, sorrow might wear

For her own comforting: or some long-fringed cloth

In which a new-born and unwelcome babe

Might wail unheeded; or a dainty sheet

Which, delicately perfumed with sweet herbs,

Might serve to wrap a dead man. Spin what you will;

I care not, I.

Bianca. The brittle thread is broken,

The dull wheel wearies of its ceaseless round,

The duller distaff sickens of its load;

I will not spin to-night.

Simone. It matters not.

To-morrow you shall spin, and every day

Shall find you at your distaff. So Lucretia

Was found by Tarquin. So, perchance, Lucretia

Waited for Tarquin. Who knows? I have heard

Strange things about men's wives. And now, my lord,

What news abroad? I heard to-day at Pisa

That certain of the English merchants there

Would sell their woollens at a lower rate

Than the just laws allow, and have entreated

The Signory to hear them.

Is this well?

Should merchant be to merchant as a wolf?

And should the stranger living in our land

Seek by enforced privilege or craft

To rob us of our profits?

Guido. What should I do

With merchants or their profits? Shall I go

And wrangle with the Signory on your count?

And wear the gown in which you buy from fools,

Or sell to sillier bidders? Honest Simone,

Wool-selling or wool-gathering is for you.

My wits have other quarries.

Bianca. Noble Lord,

I pray you pardon my good husband here,

His soul stands ever in the market-place,

And his heart beats but at the price of wool.

Yet he is honest in his common way.

[To SIMONE]

And you, have you no shame? A gracious Prince

Comes to our house, and you must weary him

With most misplaced assurance. Ask his pardon.

Simone. I ask it humbly. We will talk to-night

Of other things. I hear the Holy Father

Has sent a letter to the King of France

Bidding him cross that shield of snow, the Alps,

And make a peace in Italy, which will be

Worse than a war of brothers, and more bloody

Than civil rapine or intestine feuds.

Guido. Oh! we are weary of that King of France,

Who never comes, but ever talks of coming.

What are these things to me? There are other things

Closer, and of more import, good Simone.

Bianca [*To Simone*]. I think you tire our most gracious guest.

What is the King of France to us? As much

As are your English merchants with their wool.

* * * * *

Simone. Is it so then? Is all this mighty world

Narrowed into the confines of this room

With but three souls for poor inhabitants?

Ay! there are times when the great universe,

Like cloth in some unskilful dyer's vat,

Shrivels into a handbreadth, and perchance

That time is now! Well! let that time be now.

Let this mean room be as that mighty stage

Whereon kings die, and our ignoble lives

Become the stakes God plays for.

I do not know

Why I speak thus. My ride has wearied me.

And my horse stumbled thrice, which is an omen

That bodes not good to any.

Alas! my lord,

How poor a bargain is this life of man,

And in how mean a market are we sold!

When we are born our mothers weep, but when

We die there is none weeps for us. No, not one.

[*Passes to back of stage.*]

Bianca. How like a common chapman does he speak!

I hate him, soul and body. Cowardice

Has set her pale seal on his brow. His hands

Whiter than poplar leaves in windy springs,

Shake with some palsy; and his stammering mouth

Blurts out a foolish froth of empty words

Like water from a conduit.

Guido. Sweet Bianca,

He is not worthy of your thought or mine.

The man is but a very honest knave

Full of fine phrases for life's merchandise,

Selling most dear what he must hold most cheap,

A windy brawler in a world of words.

I never met so eloquent a fool.

Bianca. Oh, would that Death might take him where he stands!

Simone [*turning round*]. Who spake of Death? Let no one speak of
Death.

What should Death do in such a merry house,

With but a wife, a husband, and a friend

To give it greeting? Let Death go to houses

Where there are vile, adulterous things, chaste wives

Who growing weary of their noble lords

Draw back the curtains of their marriage beds,

And in polluted and dishonoured sheets

Feed some unlawful lust. Ay! 'tis so

Strange, and yet so. You do not know the world.

You are too single and too honourable.

I know it well. And would it were not so,

But wisdom comes with winters. My hair grows grey,

And youth has left my body. Enough of that.

To-night is ripe for pleasure, and indeed,

I would be merry as beseems a host

Who finds a gracious and unlooked-for guest

Waiting to greet him. [*Takes up a lute.*]

But what is this, my lord?

Why, you have brought a lute to play to us.

Oh! play, sweet Prince. And, if I am too bold,

Pardon, but play.

Guido. I will not play to-night.

Some other night, Simone.

[To Bianca] You and I

Together, with no listeners but the stars,

Or the more jealous moon.

Simone. Nay, but my lord!

Nay, but I do beseech you. For I have heard

That by the simple fingering of a string,

Or delicate breath breathed along hollowed reeds,

Or blown into cold mouths of cunning bronze,

Those who are curious in this art can draw

Poor souls from prison-houses. I have heard also

How such strange magic lurks within these shells

That at their bidding casements open wide

And Innocence puts vine-leaves in her hair,

And wantons like a mænad. Let that pass.

Your lute I know is chaste. And therefore play:

Ravish my ears with some sweet melody;

My soul is in a prison-house, and needs

Music to cure its madness. Good Bianca,

Entreat our guest to play.

Bianca. Be not afraid,

Our well-loved guest will choose his place and moment:

That moment is not now. You weary him

With your uncouth insistence.

Guido. Honest Simone,

Some other night. To-night I am content

With the low music of Bianca's voice,

Who, when she speaks, charms the too amorous air,

And makes the reeling earth stand still, or fix

His cycle round her beauty.

Simone. You flatter her.

She has her virtues as most women have,

But beauty in a gem she may not wear.

It is better so, perchance.

Well, my dear lord,

If you will not draw melodies from your lute

To charm my moody and o'er-troubled soul

You'll drink with me at least?

[*Motioning* Guido *to his own place.*]

Your place is laid.

Fetch me a stool, Bianca. Close the shutters.

Set the great bar across. I would not have

The curious world with its small prying eyes

To peer upon our pleasure.

Now, my lord,

Give us a toast from a full brimming cup.

[*Starts back.*]

What is this stain upon the cloth? It looks

As purple as a wound upon Christ's side.

Wine merely is it? I have heard it said

When wine is spilt blood is spilt also,

But that's a foolish tale.

My lord, I trust

My grape is to your liking? The wine of Naples

Is fiery like its mountains. Our Tuscan vineyards

Yield a more wholesome juice.

Guido. I like it well,

Honest Simone; and, with your good leave,

Will toast the fair Bianca when her lips

Have like red rose-leaves floated on this cup

And left its vintage sweeter. Taste, Bianca.

[Bianca *drinks.*]

Oh, all the honey of Hyblean bees,

Matched with this draught were bitter!

Good Simone,

You do not share the feast.

Simone. It is strange, my lord,

I cannot eat or drink with you, to-night.

Some humour, or some fever in my blood,

At other seasons temperate, or some thought

That like an adder creeps from point to point,

That like a madman crawls from cell to cell,

Poisons my palate and makes appetite

A loathing, not a longing.

[*Goes aside.*]

Guido. Sweet Bianca,

This common chapman wearies me with words.

I must go hence. To-morrow I will come.

Tell me the hour.

Bianca. Come with the youngest dawn!

Until I see you all my life is vain.

Guido. Ah! loose the falling midnight of your hair,

And in those stars, your eyes, let me behold

Mine image, as in mirrors. Dear Bianca,

Though it be but a shadow, keep me there,

Nor gaze at anything that does not show

Some symbol of my semblance. I am jealous

Of what your vision feasts on.

Bianca. Oh! be sure

Your image will be with me always. Dear

Love can translate the very meanest thing

Into a sign of sweet remembrances.

But come before the lark with its shrill song

Has waked a world of dreamers. I will stand

Upon the balcony.

Guido. And by a ladder

Wrought out of scarlet silk and sewn with pearls

Will come to meet me. White foot after foot,

Like snow upon a rose-tree.

Bianca. As you will.

You know that I am yours for love or Death.

Guido. Simone, I must go to mine own house.

Simone. So soon? Why should you? The great Duomo's bell

Has not yet tolled its midnight, and the watchmen

Who with their hollow horns mock the pale moon,

Lie drowsy in their towers. Stay awhile.

I fear we may not see you here again,

And that fear saddens my too simple heart.

Guido. Be not afraid, Simone. I will stand

Most constant in my friendship, But to-night

I go to mine own home, and that at once.

To-morrow, sweet Bianca.

Simone. Well, well, so be it.

I would have wished for fuller converse with you,

My new friend, my honourable guest,

But that it seems may not be.

And besides

I do not doubt your father waits for you,

Wearying for voice or footstep. You, I think,

Are his one child? He has no other child.

You are the gracious pillar of his house,

The flower of a garden full of weeds.

Your father's nephews do not love him well

So run folks' tongues in Florence. I meant but that.

Men say they envy your inheritance

And look upon your vineyards with fierce eyes

As Ahab looked on Naboth's goodly field.

But that is but the chatter of a town

Where women talk too much.

Good-night, my lord.

Fetch a pine torch, Bianca. The old staircase

Is full of pitfalls, and the churlish moon

Grows, like a miser, niggard of her beams,

And hides her face behind a muslin mask

As harlots do when they go forth to snare

Some wretched soul in sin. Now, I will get

Your cloak and sword. Nay, pardon, my good Lord,

It is but meet that I should wait on you

Who have so honoured my poor burgher's house,

Drunk of my wine, and broken bread, and made

Yourself a sweet familiar. Oftentimes

My wife and I will talk of this fair night

And its great issues.

Why, what a sword is this.

Ferrara's temper, pliant as a snake,

And deadlier, I doubt not. With such steel,

One need fear nothing in the moil of life.

I never touched so delicate a blade.

I have a sword too, somewhat rusted now.

We men of peace are taught humility,

And to bear many burdens on our backs,

And not to murmur at an unjust world,

And to endure unjust indignities.

We are taught that, and like the patient Jew

Find profit in our pain.

Yet I remember

How once upon the road to Padua

A robber sought to take my pack-horse from me,

I slit his throat and left him. I can bear

Dishonour, public insult, many shames,

Shrill scorn, and open contumely, but he

Who filches from me something that is mine,

Ay! though it be the meanest trencher-plate

From which I feed mine appetite—oh! he

Perils his soul and body in the theft

And dies for his small sin. From what strange clay

We men are moulded!

Guido. Why do you speak like this?

Simone. I wonder, my Lord Guido, if my sword

Is better tempered than this steel of yours?

Shall we make trial? Or is my state too low

For you to cross your rapier against mine,

In jest, or earnest?

Guido. Naught would please me better

Than to stand fronting you with naked blade

In jest, or earnest. Give me mine own sword.

Fetch yours. To-night will settle the great issue

Whether the Prince's or the merchant's steel

Is better tempered. Was not that your word?

Fetch your own sword. Why do you tarry, sir?

Simone. My lord, of all the gracious courtesies

That you have showered on my barren house

This is the highest.

Bianca, fetch my sword.

Thrust back that stool and table. We must have

An open circle for our match at arms,

And good Bianca here shall hold the torch

Lest what is but a jest grow serious.

Bianca [*To Guido*]. Oh! kill him, kill him!

Simone. Hold the torch, Bianca.

[*They begin to fight.*]

Simone. Have at you! Ah! Ha! would you?

[*He is wounded by* Guido.]

A scratch, no more. The torch was in mine eyes.

Do not look sad, Bianca. It is nothing.

Your husband bleeds, 'tis nothing. Take a cloth,

Bind it about mine arm. Nay, not so tight.

More softly, my good wife. And be not sad,

I pray you be not sad. No; take it off.

What matter if I bleed?

[*Tears bandage off.*]

Again! again!

[Simone *disarms* Guido]

My gentle Lord, you see that I was right

My sword is better tempered, finer steel,

But let us match our daggers.

Bianca [*to Guido*]

Kill him! kill him!

Simone. Put out the torch, Bianca.

[Bianca *puts out torch.*]

Now, my good Lord,

Now to the death of one, or both of us,

Or all three it may be. [*They fight.*]

There and there.

Ah, devil! do I hold thee in my grip?

[Simone *overpowers* Guido *and throws him down over table.*]

Guido. Fool! take your strangling fingers from my throat.

I am my father's only son; the State

Has but one heir, and that false enemy France

Waits for the ending of my father's line

To fall upon our city.

Simone. Hush! your father

When he is childless will be happier.

As for the State, I think our state of Florence

Needs no adulterous pilot at its helm.

Your life would soil its lilies.

Guido. Take off your hands

Take off your damned hands. Loose me, I say!

Simone. Nay, you are caught in such a cunning vice

That nothing will avail you, and your life

Narrowed into a single point of shame

Ends with that shame and ends most shamefully.

Guido. Oh! let me have a priest before I die!

Simone. What wouldst thou have a priest for? Tell thy sins

To God, whom thou shalt see this very night

And then no more for ever. Tell thy sins

To Him who is most just, being pitiless,

Most pitiful being just. As for myself. . .

Guido. Oh! help me, sweet Bianca! help me, Bianca,

Thou knowest I am innocent of harm.

Simone. What, is there life yet in those lying lips?

Die like a dog with lolling tongue! Die! Die!

And the dumb river shall receive your corse

And wash it all unheeded to the sea.

Guido. Lord Christ receive my wretched soul to-night!

Simone. Amen to that. Now for the other.

[*He dies.* Simone *rises and looks at* Bianca. *She comes towards him as one dazed with wonder and with outstretched arms.*]

Bianca. Why

Did you not tell me you were so strong?

Simone. Why

Did you not tell me you were beautiful?

[*He kisses her on the mouth.*]

CURTAIN

About Author

As a spokesman for aestheticism, he tried his hand at various literary activities: he published a book of poems, lectured in the United States and Canada on the new "English Renaissance in Art" and interior decoration, and then returned to London where he worked prolifically as a journalist. Known for his biting wit, flamboyant dress and glittering conversational skill, Wilde became one of the best-known personalities of his day. At the turn of the 1890s, he refined his ideas about the supremacy of art in a series of dialogues and essays, and incorporated themes of decadence, duplicity, and beauty into what would be his only novel, The Picture of Dorian Gray (1890). The opportunity to construct aesthetic details precisely, and combine them with larger social themes, drew Wilde to write drama. He wrote Salome (1891) in French while in Paris but it was refused a licence for England due to an absolute prohibition on the portrayal of Biblical subjects on the English stage. Unperturbed, Wilde produced four society comedies in the early 1890s, which made him one of the most successful playwrights of late-Victorian London.

At the height of his fame and success, while The Importance of Being Earnest (1895) was still being performed in London, Wilde had the Marquess of Queensberry prosecuted for criminal libel. The Marquess was the father of Wilde's lover, Lord Alfred Douglas. The libel trial unearthed evidence that caused Wilde to drop his charges and led to his own arrest and trial for gross indecency with men. After two more trials he was convicted and sentenced to two years' hard labour, the maximum penalty, and was jailed from 1895 to 1897. During his last year in prison, he wrote De Profundis (published posthumously in 1905), a long letter which discusses his spiritual journey through his trials, forming a dark counterpoint to his earlier philosophy of pleasure. On his release, he left immediately for France, never to return to Ireland or Britain. There he wrote his last work, The Ballad of Reading Gaol (1898), a long poem commemorating the harsh rhythms of prison life. He died destitute in Paris at the age of 46.

Early life

Oscar Wilde was born at 21 Westland Row, Dublin (now home of the Oscar Wilde Centre, Trinity College), the second of three children born to Sir William Wilde and Jane Wilde, two years behind William ("Willie"). Wilde's mother had distant Italian ancestry, and under the pseudonym "Speranza" (the Italian word for 'hope'), wrote poetry for the revolutionary Young Irelanders in 1848; she was a lifelong Irish nationalist. She read the Young Irelanders' poetry to Oscar and Willie, inculcating a love of these poets in her sons. Lady Wilde's interest in the neo-classical revival showed in the paintings and busts of ancient Greece and Rome in her home.

William Wilde was Ireland's leading oto-ophthalmologic (ear and eye) surgeon and was knighted in 1864 for his services as medical adviser and assistant commissioner to the censuses of Ireland. He also wrote books about Irish archaeology and peasant folklore. A renowned philanthropist, his dispensary for the care of the city's poor at the rear of Trinity College, Dublin, was the forerunner of the Dublin Eye and Ear Hospital, now located at Adelaide Road. On his father's side Wilde was descended from a Dutchman, Colonel de Wilde, who went to Ireland with King William of Orange's invading army in 1690. On his mother's side Wilde's ancestors included a bricklayer from County Durham who emigrated to Ireland sometime in the 1770s.

Wilde was baptised as an infant in St. Mark's Church, Dublin, the local Church of Ireland (Anglican) church. When the church was closed, the records were moved to the nearby St. Ann's Church, Dawson Street. Davis Coakley mentions a second baptism by a Catholic priest, Father Prideaux Fox, who befriended Oscar's mother circa 1859. According to Fox's own testimony in Donahoe's Magazine in 1905, Jane Wilde would visit his chapel in Glencree, County Wicklow, for Mass and would take her sons with her. She then asked Father Fox to baptise her sons. Fox described it in this way:

"I am not sure if she ever became a Catholic herself but it was not long before she asked me to instruct two of her children, one of them being the future erratic genius, Oscar Wilde. After a few weeks I baptized these two children, Lady Wilde herself being present on the occasion."

In addition to his children with his wife, Sir William Wilde was the father of three children born out of wedlock before his marriage: Henry Wilson, born in 1838, and Emily and Mary Wilde, born in 1847 and 1849, respectively, of different maternity to Henry. Sir William acknowledged paternity of his illegitimate children and provided for their education, but they were reared by his relatives rather than by his wife or with his legitimate children.

In 1855, the family moved to No. 1 Merrion Square, where Wilde's sister, Isola, was born in 1857. The Wildes' new home was larger and, with both his parents' sociality and success, it soon became a "unique medical and cultural milieu". Guests at their salon included Sheridan Le Fanu, Charles Lever, George Petrie, Isaac Butt, William Rowan Hamilton and Samuel Ferguson.

Until he was nine, Oscar Wilde was educated at home, where a French bonne and a German governess taught him their languages. He then attended Portora Royal School in Enniskillen, County Fermanagh from 1864 to 1871. Until his early twenties, Wilde summered at the villa, Moytura House, his father built in Cong, County Mayo. There the young Wilde and his brother Willie played with George Moore.

Isola died aged nine of meningitis. Wilde's poem "Requiescat" is written to her memory.

"Tread lightly, she is near

Under the snow

Speak gently, she can hear

the daisies grow"

University education: 1870s

Trinity College, Dublin

Wilde left Portora with a royal scholarship to read classics at Trinity College, Dublin, from 1871 to 1874, sharing rooms with his older brother Willie Wilde. Trinity, one of the leading classical schools, placed him with scholars such as R. Y. Tyrell, Arthur Palmer, Edward Dowden and his tutor, Professor J. P. Mahaffy who inspired his interest in Greek literature. As a student Wilde worked with Mahaffy on the latter's book Social Life in Greece. Wilde, despite later reservations, called Mahaffy "my first and best teacher" and "the scholar who showed me how to love Greek things". For his part, Mahaffy boasted of having created Wilde; later, he named him "the only blot on my tutorship".

The University Philosophical Society also provided an education, discussing intellectual and artistic subjects such as Rossetti and Swinburne weekly. Wilde quickly became an established member – the members' suggestion book for 1874 contains two pages of banter (sportingly) mocking Wilde's emergent aestheticism. He presented a paper titled "Aesthetic Morality". At Trinity, Wilde established himself as an outstanding student: he came first in his class in his first year, won a scholarship by competitive examination in his second, and then, in his finals, won the Berkeley Gold Medal, the University's highest academic award in Greek. He was encouraged to compete for a demyship to Magdalen College, Oxford – which he won easily, having already studied Greek for over nine years.

Magdalen College, Oxford

At Magdalen, he read Greats from 1874 to 1878, and from there he applied to join the Oxford Union, but failed to be elected.

Oscar Wilde posing for a photograph, looking at the camera. He is wearing a checked suit and a bowler hat. His right foot is resting on a knee high bench, and his right hand, holding gloves, is on it. The left hand is in the pocket.

Attracted by its dress, secrecy, and ritual, Wilde petitioned the Apollo Masonic Lodge at Oxford, and was soon raised to the "Sublime Degree of Master Mason". During a resurgent interest in Freemasonry in his third year, he commented he "would be awfully sorry to give it up if I secede from the

Protestant Heresy". Wilde's active involvement in Freemasonry lasted only for the time he spent at Oxford and his membership of the Apollo University Lodge lapsed after non-payment of subscriptions. He was deeply considering converting to Catholicism, discussing the possibility with clergy several times. In 1877, Wilde was left speechless after an audience with Pope Pius IX in Rome. He eagerly read Cardinal Newman's books, and became more serious in 1878, when he met the Reverend Sebastian Bowden, a priest in the Brompton Oratory who had received some high-profile converts. Neither his father, who threatened to cut off his funds, nor Mahaffy thought much of the plan; but mostly Wilde, the supreme individualist, balked at the last minute from pledging himself to any formal creed. On the appointed day of his baptism, Father Bowden received a bunch of altar lilies instead. Wilde retained a lifelong interest in Catholic theology and liturgy.

While at Magdalen College, Wilde became particularly well known for his role in the aesthetic and decadent movements. He wore his hair long, openly scorned "manly" sports though he occasionally boxed, and decorated his rooms with peacock feathers, lilies, sunflowers, blue china and other objets d'art, once remarking to friends whom he entertained lavishly, "I find it harder and harder every day to live up to my blue china." The line quickly became famous, accepted as a slogan by aesthetes but used against them by critics who sensed in it a terrible vacuousness. Some elements disdained the aesthetes, but their languishing attitudes and showy costumes became a recognised pose. Wilde was once physically attacked by a group of four fellow students, and dealt with them single-handedly, surprising critics. By his third year Wilde had truly begun to create himself and his myth, and saw his learning developing in much larger ways than merely the prescribed texts. This attitude resulted in his being rusticated for one term, when he nonchalantly returned to college late from a trip to Greece with Mahaffy.

Wilde did not meet Walter Pater until his third year, but had been enthralled by his Studies in the History of the Renaissance, published during Wilde's final year in Trinity. Pater argued that man's sensibility to beauty should be refined above all else, and that each moment should be felt to its fullest extent. Years later, in De Profundis, Wilde called Pater's Studies...

"that book that has had such a strange influence over my life". He learned tracts of the book by heart, and carried it with him on travels in later years. Pater gave Wilde his sense of almost flippant devotion to art, though it was John Ruskin who gave him a purpose for it. Ruskin despaired at the self-validating aestheticism of Pater, arguing that the importance of art lies in its potential for the betterment of society. Ruskin admired beauty, but believed it must be allied with, and applied to, moral good. When Wilde eagerly attended Ruskin's lecture series The Aesthetic and Mathematic Schools of Art in Florence, he learned about aesthetics as simply the non-mathematical elements of painting. Despite being given to neither early rising nor manual labour, Wilde volunteered for Ruskin's project to convert a swampy country lane into a smart road neatly edged with flowers.

Wilde won the 1878 Newdigate Prize for his poem "Ravenna", which reflected on his visit there the year before, and he duly read it at Encaenia. In November 1878, he graduated with a double first in his B.A. of Classical Moderations and Literae Humaniores (Greats). Wilde wrote to a friend, "The dons are 'astonied' beyond words – the Bad Boy doing so well in the end!"

Apprenticeship of an aesthete: 1880s

Debut in society

After graduation from Oxford, Wilde returned to Dublin, where he met again Florence Balcombe, a childhood sweetheart. She became engaged to Bram Stoker and they married in 1878. Wilde was disappointed but stoic: he wrote to her, remembering "the two sweet years – the sweetest years of all my youth" they had spent together. He also stated his intention to "return to England, probably for good." This he did in 1878, only briefly visiting Ireland twice.

Unsure of his next step, he wrote to various acquaintances enquiring about Classics positions at Oxford or Cambridge. The Rise of Historical Criticism was his submission for the Chancellor's Essay prize of 1879, which, though no longer a student, he was still eligible to enter. Its subject, "Historical Criticism among the Ancients" seemed ready-made for Wilde – with both his skill in composition and ancient learning – but he struggled to find his voice with the long, flat, scholarly style. Unusually, no prize was awarded that year. With the last of his inheritance from the sale of his father's houses, he set himself up as a bachelor in London. The 1881 British Census listed Wilde as a boarder at 1 (now 44) Tite Street, Chelsea, where Frank Miles, a society painter, was the head of the household. Wilde spent the next six years in London and Paris, and in the United States where he travelled to deliver lectures.

He had been publishing lyrics and poems in magazines since entering Trinity College, especially in Kottabos and the Dublin University Magazine. In mid-1881, at 27 years old, Poems collected, revised and expanded his poetic efforts. The book was generally well received, and sold out its first print run of 750 copies, prompting further printings in 1882. It was bound in a rich, enamel, parchment cover (embossed with gilt blossom) and printed on hand-made Dutch paper; Wilde presented many copies to the dignitaries and writers who received him over the next few years. The Oxford Union condemned the book for alleged plagiarism in a tight vote. The librarian, who had requested the book for the library, returned the presentation copy to Wilde with a note of apology. Richard Ellmann argues that Wilde's poem "Hélas!" was a sincere, though flamboyant, attempt to explain the dichotomies he saw in himself:

To drift with every passion till my soul

Is a stringed lute on which all winds can play

Punch was less enthusiastic, "The poet is Wilde, but his poetry's tame" was their verdict.

America: 1882

Aestheticism was sufficiently in vogue to be caricatured by Gilbert and Sullivan in Patience (1881). Richard D'Oyly Carte, an English impresario, invited Wilde to make a lecture tour of North America, simultaneously priming the pump for the US tour of Patience and selling this most charming aesthete to the American public. Wilde journeyed on the SS Arizona, arriving 2 January 1882, and disembarking the following day. Originally planned to last four months, it continued for almost a year due to the commercial success. Wilde sought to transpose the beauty he saw in art into daily life. This was a practical as well as philosophical project: in Oxford he had surrounded himself with blue china and lilies, and now one of his lectures was on interior design.

When asked to explain reports that he had paraded down Piccadilly in London carrying a lily, long hair flowing, Wilde replied, "It's not whether I did it or not that's important, but whether people believed I did it". Wilde believed that the artist should hold forth higher ideals, and that pleasure and beauty would replace utilitarian ethics.

Wilde and aestheticism were both mercilessly caricatured and criticised in the press; the Springfield Republican, for instance, commented on Wilde's behaviour during his visit to Boston to lecture on aestheticism, suggesting that Wilde's conduct was more a bid for notoriety rather than devotion to beauty and the aesthetic. T. W. Higginson, a cleric and abolitionist, wrote in "Unmanly Manhood" of his general concern that Wilde, "whose only distinction is that he has written a thin volume of very mediocre verse", would improperly influence the behaviour of men and women.

According to biographer Michèle Mendelssohn, Wilde was the subject of anti-Irish caricature and was portrayed as a monkey, a blackface performer and a Christy minstrel throughout his career. "Harper's Weekly put a sunflower-worshipping monkey dressed as Wilde on the front of the January 1882 issue. The magazine didn't let its reputation for quality impede its expression of what are now considered odious ethnic and racial ideologies. The drawing stimulated other American maligners and, in England, had a full page reprint in the Lady's Pictorial. ... When the National Republican discussed Wilde, it was to explain 'a few items as to the animal's pedigree.' And on 22 January 1882 the Washington Post illustrated the Wild Man of Borneo alongside Oscar Wilde of England and asked 'How far is it from this to this?' " Though his press reception was hostile, Wilde was well received in diverse settings across America; he drank whiskey with miners in Leadville, Colorado, and was fêted at the most fashionable salons in many cities he visited.

London life and marriage

70

His earnings, plus expected income from The Duchess of Padua, allowed him to move to Paris between February and mid-May 1883. While there he met Robert Sherard, whom he entertained constantly. "We are dining on the Duchess tonight", Wilde would declare before taking him to an expensive restaurant. In August he briefly returned to New York for the production of Vera, his first play, after it was turned down in London. He reportedly entertained the other passengers with "Ave Imperatrix!, A Poem on England", about the rise and fall of empires. E. C. Stedman, in Victorian Poets describes this "lyric to England" as "manly verse – a poetic and eloquent invocation". The play was initially well received by the audience, but when the critics wrote lukewarm reviews attendance fell sharply and the play closed a week after it had opened.

Wilde was left to return to England and lecturing on topics including Personal Impressions of America, The Value of Art in Modern Life, and Dress.

In London, he had been introduced in 1881 to Constance Lloyd, daughter of Horace Lloyd, a wealthy Queen's Counsel. She happened to be visiting Dublin in 1884, when Wilde was lecturing at the Gaiety Theatre. He proposed to her, and they married on 29 May 1884 at the Anglican St James's Church, Paddington in London. Constance's annual allowance of £250 was generous for a young woman (equivalent to about £25,600 in current value), but the Wildes had relatively luxurious tastes, and they had preached to others for so long on the subject of design that people expected their home to set new standards. No. 16, Tite Street was duly renovated in seven months at considerable expense. The couple had two sons, Cyril (1885) and Vyvyan (1886). Wilde became the sole literary signatory of George Bernard Shaw's petition for a pardon of the anarchists arrested (and later executed) after the Haymarket massacre in Chicago in 1886.

Robert Ross had read Wilde's poems before they met, and was unrestrained by the Victorian prohibition against homosexuality, even to the extent of estranging himself from his family. By Richard Ellmann's account, he was a precocious seventeen-year-old who "so young and yet so knowing, was determined to seduce Wilde". According to Daniel Mendelsohn, Wilde, who had long alluded to Greek love, was "initiated into homosexual sex" by Ross, while his "marriage had begun to unravel after his wife's second pregnancy, which left him physically repelled".

Prose writing: 1886–91

Journalism and editorship: 1886–89

Criticism over artistic matters in The Pall Mall Gazette provoked a letter in self-defence, and soon Wilde was a contributor to that and other journals during 1885–87. He enjoyed reviewing and journalism; the form suited his style. He could organise and share his views on art, literature and life, yet in a format less tedious than lecturing. Buoyed up, his reviews were largely chatty and positive. Wilde, like his parents before him, also supported the cause of Irish Nationalism. When Charles Stewart Parnell was falsely accused of inciting murder Wilde wrote a series of astute columns defending him in the Daily Chronicle.

His flair, having previously only been put into socialising, suited journalism and did not go unnoticed. With his youth nearly over, and a family to support, in mid-1887 Wilde became the editor of The Lady's World magazine, his name prominently appearing on the cover. He promptly renamed it The Woman's World and raised its tone, adding serious articles on parenting, culture, and politics, keeping discussions of fashion and arts. Two pieces of fiction were usually included, one to be read to children, the other for the ladies themselves. Wilde worked hard to solicit good contributions from his wide artistic acquaintance, including those of Lady Wilde and his wife Constance, while his own "Literary and Other Notes" were themselves popular and amusing.

The initial vigour and excitement he brought to the job began to fade as administration, commuting and office life became tedious. At the same time as Wilde's interest flagged, the publishers became concerned anew about circulation: sales, at the relatively high price of one shilling, remained low. Increasingly sending instructions to the magazine by letter, he began a new period of creative work and his own column appeared less regularly. In October 1889, Wilde had finally found his voice in prose and, at the end of the second volume, Wilde left The Woman's World. The magazine outlasted him by one issue.

If Wilde's period at the helm of the magazine was a mixed success from an organizational point of view, one can also argue that it played a pivotal role in his development as a writer and facilitated his ascent to fame. Whilst Wilde the journalist supplied articles under the guidance of his editors, Wilde the editor is forced to learn to manipulate the literary marketplace on his own terms.

Shorter fiction

Wilde published The Happy Prince and Other Tales in 1888, and had been regularly writing fairy stories for magazines. In 1891 he published two more collections, Lord Arthur Savile's Crime and Other Stories, and in September A House of Pomegranates was dedicated "To Constance Mary Wilde". "The Portrait of Mr. W. H.", which Wilde had begun in 1887, was first published in Blackwood's Edinburgh Magazine in July 1889. It is a short story, which reports a conversation, in which the theory that Shakespeare's sonnets were written out of the poet's love of the boy actor "Willie Hughes", is advanced, retracted, and then propounded again. The only evidence for this is two supposed puns within the sonnets themselves.

The anonymous narrator is at first sceptical, then believing, finally flirtatious with the reader: he concludes that "there is really a great deal to be said of the Willie Hughes theory of Shakespeare's sonnets." By the end fact and fiction have melded together. Arthur Ransome wrote that Wilde "read something of himself into Shakespeare's sonnets" and became fascinated with the "Willie Hughes theory" despite the lack of biographical evidence for the historical William Hughes' existence. Instead of writing a short but serious essay on the question, Wilde tossed the theory amongst the three characters of the story, allowing it to unfold as background to the plot. The story thus is an early masterpiece of Wilde's combining many elements that interested him: conversation, literature and the idea that to shed oneself of an idea one must first convince another of its truth. Ransome concludes that Wilde succeeds precisely because the literary criticism is unveiled with such a deft touch.

Though containing nothing but "special pleading", it would not, he says "be possible to build an airier castle in Spain than this of the imaginary William Hughes" we continue listening nonetheless to be charmed by the telling. "You must believe in Willie Hughes," Wilde told an acquaintance, "I almost do, myself."

Essays and dialogues

Wilde, having tired of journalism, had been busy setting out his aesthetic ideas more fully in a series of longer prose pieces which were published in the major literary-intellectual journals of the day. In January 1889, The Decay of Lying: A Dialogue appeared in The Nineteenth Century, and Pen, Pencil and Poison, a satirical biography of Thomas Griffiths Wainewright, in The Fortnightly Review, edited by Wilde's friend Frank Harris. Two of Wilde's four writings on aesthetics are dialogues: though Wilde had evolved professionally from lecturer to writer, he retained an oral tradition of sorts. Having always excelled as a wit and raconteur, he often composed by assembling phrases, bons mots and witticisms into a longer, cohesive work.

Wilde was concerned about the effect of moralising on art; he believed in art's redemptive, developmental powers: "Art is individualism, and individualism is a disturbing and disintegrating force. There lies its immense value. For what it seeks is to disturb monotony of type, slavery of custom, tyranny of habit, and the reduction of man to the level of a machine." In his only political text, The Soul of Man Under Socialism, he argued political conditions should establish this primacy – private property should be abolished, and cooperation should be substituted for competition. At the same time, he stressed that the government most amenable to artists was no government at all. Wilde envisioned a society where mechanisation has freed human effort from the burden of necessity, effort which can instead be expended on artistic creation. George Orwell summarised, "In effect, the world will be populated by artists, each striving after perfection in the way that seems best to him."

This point of view did not align him with the Fabians, intellectual socialists who advocated using state apparatus to change social conditions, nor did it endear him to the monied classes whom he had previously entertained.

Hesketh Pearson, introducing a collection of Wilde's essays in 1950, remarked how The Soul of Man Under Socialism had been an inspirational text for revolutionaries in Tsarist Russia but laments that in the Stalinist era "it is doubtful whether there are any uninspected places in which it could now be hidden".

Wilde considered including this pamphlet and The Portrait of Mr. W.H., his essay-story on Shakespeare's sonnets, in a new anthology in 1891, but eventually decided to limit it to purely aesthetic subjects. Intentions packaged revisions of four essays: The Decay of Lying, Pen, Pencil and Poison, The Truth of Masks (first published 1885), and The Critic as Artist in two parts. For Pearson the biographer, the essays and dialogues exhibit every aspect of Wilde's genius and character: wit, romancer, talker, lecturer, humanist and scholar and concludes that "no other productions of his have as varied an appeal". 1891 turned out to be Wilde's annus mirabilis; apart from his three collections he also produced his only novel.

The Picture of Dorian Gray

The first version of The Picture of Dorian Gray was published as the lead story in the July 1890 edition of Lippincott's Monthly Magazine, along with five others. The story begins with a man painting a picture of Gray. When Gray, who has a "face like ivory and rose leaves", sees his finished portrait, he breaks down. Distraught that his beauty will fade while the portrait stays beautiful, he inadvertently makes a Faustian bargain in which only the painted image grows old while he stays beautiful and young. For Wilde, the purpose of art would be to guide life as if beauty alone were its object. As Gray's portrait allows him to escape the corporeal ravages of his hedonism, Wilde sought to juxtapose the beauty he saw in art with daily life.

Reviewers immediately criticised the novel's decadence and homosexual allusions; The Daily Chronicle for example, called it "unclean", "poisonous", and "heavy with the mephitic odours of moral and spiritual putrefaction". Wilde vigorously responded, writing to the editor of the Scots Observer, in which he clarified his stance on ethics and aesthetics in art – "If a work of art is rich and vital and complete, those who have artistic instincts will see its beauty and those to whom ethics appeal more strongly will see its moral lesson." He nevertheless revised it extensively for book publication in 1891: six new chapters were added, some overtly decadent passages and homo-eroticism excised, and a preface was included consisting of twenty two epigrams, such as "Books are well written, or badly written. That is all."

Contemporary reviewers and modern critics have postulated numerous possible sources of the story, a search Jershua McCormack argues is futile because Wilde "has tapped a root of Western folklore so deep and ubiquitous that the story has escaped its origins and returned to the oral tradition." Wilde claimed the plot was "an idea that is as old as the history of literature but to which I have given a new form". Modern critic Robin McKie considered the novel to be technically mediocre, saying that the conceit of the plot had guaranteed its fame, but the device is never pushed to its full.

Theatrical career: 1892–95

Salomé

The 1891 census records the Wildes' residence at 16 Tite Street, where he lived with his wife Constance and two sons. Wilde though, not content with being better known than ever in London, returned to Paris in October 1891, this time as a respected writer. He was received at the salons littéraires, including the famous mardis of Stéphane Mallarmé, a renowned symbolist poet of the time. Wilde's two plays during the 1880s, Vera; or, The Nihilists and The Duchess of Padua, had not met with much success. He had continued his interest in the theatre and now, after finding his voice in prose, his thoughts turned again to the dramatic form as the biblical iconography of Salome filled his mind. One evening, after discussing depictions of Salome throughout history, he returned to his hotel and noticed a blank copybook lying on the desk, and it occurred to him to write in it what he had been saying. The result was a new play, Salomé, written rapidly and in French.

A tragedy, it tells the story of Salome, the stepdaughter of the tetrarch Herod Antipas, who, to her stepfather's dismay but mother's delight, requests the head of Jokanaan (John the Baptist) on a silver platter as a reward for dancing the Dance of the Seven Veils. When Wilde returned to London just before Christmas the Paris Echo referred to him as "le great event" of the season. Rehearsals of the play, starring Sarah Bernhardt, began but the play was refused a licence by the Lord Chamberlain, since it depicted biblical characters. Salome was published jointly in Paris and London in 1893, but was not performed until 1896 in Paris, during Wilde's later incarceration.

Comedies of society

Wilde, who had first set out to irritate Victorian society with his dress and talking points, then outrage it with Dorian Gray, his novel of vice hidden beneath art, finally found a way to critique society on its own terms. Lady Windermere's Fan was first performed on 20 February 1892 at St James's Theatre, packed with the cream of society. On the surface a witty comedy, there is subtle subversion underneath: "it concludes with collusive concealment rather than collective disclosure". The audience, like Lady Windermere, are forced to soften harsh social codes in favour of a more nuanced view. The play was enormously popular, touring the country for months, but largely trashed by conservative critics. It was followed by A Woman of No Importance in 1893, another Victorian comedy, revolving around the spectre of illegitimate births, mistaken identities and late revelations. Wilde was commissioned to write two more plays and An Ideal Husband, written in 1894, followed in January 1895.

Peter Raby said these essentially English plays were well-pitched, "Wilde, with one eye on the dramatic genius of Ibsen, and the other on the commercial competition in London's West End, targeted his audience with adroit precision".

Queensberry family

In mid-1891 Lionel Johnson introduced Wilde to Lord Alfred Douglas, Johnson's cousin and an undergraduate at Oxford at the time. Known to his family and friends as "Bosie", he was a handsome and spoilt young man. An intimate friendship sprang up between Wilde and Douglas and by 1893 Wilde was infatuated with Douglas and they consorted together regularly in a tempestuous affair. If Wilde was relatively indiscreet, even flamboyant, in the way he acted, Douglas was reckless in public. Wilde, who was earning up to

£100 a week from his plays (his salary at The Woman's World had been £6), indulged Douglas's every whim: material, artistic or sexual.

Douglas soon initiated Wilde into the Victorian underground of gay prostitution and Wilde was introduced to a series of young working-class male prostitutes from 1892 onwards by Alfred Taylor. These infrequent rendezvous usually took the same form: Wilde would meet the boy, offer him gifts, dine him privately and then take him to a hotel room. Unlike Wilde's idealised, pederastic relations with Ross, John Gray, and Douglas, all of whom remained part of his aesthetic circle, these consorts were uneducated and knew nothing of literature. Soon his public and private lives had become sharply divided; in De Profundis he wrote to Douglas that "It was like feasting with panthers; the danger was half the excitement... I did not know that when they were to strike at me it was to be at another's piping and at another's pay."

Douglas and some Oxford friends founded a journal, The Chameleon, to which Wilde "sent a page of paradoxes originally destined for the Saturday Review". "Phrases and Philosophies for the Use of the Young" was to come under attack six months later at Wilde's trial, where he was forced to defend the magazine to which he had sent his work. In any case, it became unique: The Chameleon was not published again.

Lord Alfred's father, the Marquess of Queensberry, was known for his outspoken atheism, brutish manner and creation of the modern rules of boxing. Queensberry, who feuded regularly with his son, confronted Wilde and Lord Alfred about the nature of their relationship several times, but Wilde was able to mollify him. In June 1894, he called on Wilde at 16 Tite Street, without an appointment, and clarified his stance: "I do not say that you are it, but you look it, and pose at it, which is just as bad. And if I catch you and my son again in any public restaurant I will thrash you" to which Wilde responded: "I don't know what the Queensberry rules are, but the Oscar Wilde rule is to shoot on sight". His account in De Profundis was less triumphant: "It was when, in my library at Tite Street, waving his small hands in the air in epileptic fury, your father... stood uttering every foul word his foul mind could think of, and screaming the loathsome threats he afterwards with such cunning carried out". Queensberry only described the scene once, saying Wilde had "shown him the white feather", meaning he had acted in a cowardly way. Though trying to remain calm, Wilde saw that he was becoming ensnared in a brutal family quarrel. He did not wish to bear Queensberry's insults, but he knew to confront him could lead to disaster were his liaisons disclosed publicly.

The Importance of Being Earnest

Wilde's final play again returns to the theme of switched identities: the play's two protagonists engage in "bunburying" (the maintenance of alternative personas in the town and country) which allows them to escape Victorian social mores. Earnest is even lighter in tone than Wilde's earlier comedies. While their characters often rise to serious themes in moments of crisis, Earnest lacks the by-now stock Wildean characters: there is no "woman with a past", the principals are neither villainous nor cunning, simply idle cultivés, and the idealistic young women are not that innocent. Mostly set in drawing rooms and almost completely lacking in action or violence, Earnest lacks the self-conscious decadence found in The Picture of Dorian Gray and Salome.

The play, now considered Wilde's masterpiece, was rapidly written in Wilde's artistic maturity in late 1894. It was first performed on 14 February 1895, at St James's Theatre in London, Wilde's second collaboration with George Alexander, the actor-manager. Both author and producer assiduously revised, prepared and rehearsed every line, scene and setting in the months before the premiere, creating a carefully constructed representation of late-Victorian society, yet simultaneously mocking it. During rehearsal Alexander requested that Wilde shorten the play from four acts to three, which the author did. Premieres at St James's seemed like "brilliant parties", and the opening of The Importance of Being Earnest was no exception. Allan Aynesworth (who played Algernon) recalled to Hesketh Pearson, "In my fifty-three years of acting, I never remember a greater triumph than [that] first night." Earnest's immediate reception as Wilde's best work to date finally crystallised his fame into a solid artistic reputation. The Importance of Being Earnest remains his most popular play.

Wilde's professional success was mirrored by an escalation in his feud with Queensberry. Queensberry had planned to insult Wilde publicly by throwing a bouquet of rotting vegetables onto the stage; Wilde was tipped off and had Queensberry barred from entering the theatre. Fifteen weeks later Wilde was in prison.

Trials

Wilde v. Queensberry

On 18 February 1895, the Marquess left his calling card at Wilde's club, the Albemarle, inscribed: "For Oscar Wilde, posing somdomite" . Wilde, encouraged by Douglas and against the advice of his friends, initiated a private prosecution against Queensberry for libel, since the note amounted to a public accusation that Wilde had committed the crime of sodomy.

Queensberry was arrested for criminal libel; a charge carrying a possible sentence of up to two years in prison. Under the 1843 Libel Act, Queensberry could avoid conviction for libel only by demonstrating that his accusation was in fact true, and furthermore that there was some "public benefit" to having made the accusation openly. Queensberry's lawyers thus hired private detectives to find evidence of Wilde's homosexual liaisons.

Wilde's friends had advised him against the prosecution at a Saturday Review meeting at the Café Royal on 24 March 1895; Frank Harris warned him that "they are going to prove sodomy against you" and advised him to flee to France. Wilde and Douglas walked out in a huff, Wilde saying "it is at such moments as these that one sees who are one's true friends". The scene was witnessed by George Bernard Shaw who recalled it to Arthur Ransome a day or so before Ransome's trial for libelling Douglas in 1913. To Ransome it confirmed what he had said in his 1912 book on Wilde; that Douglas's rivalry for Wilde with Robbie Ross and his arguments with his father had resulted in Wilde's public disaster; as Wilde wrote in De Profundis. Douglas lost his case. Shaw included an account of the argument between Harris, Douglas and Wilde in the preface to his play The Dark Lady of the Sonnets.

The libel trial became a cause célèbre as salacious details of Wilde's private life with Taylor and Douglas began to appear in the press. A team of

80

private detectives had directed Queensberry's lawyers, led by Edward Carson QC, to the world of the Victorian underground. Wilde's association with blackmailers and male prostitutes, cross-dressers and homosexual brothels was recorded, and various persons involved were interviewed, some being coerced to appear as witnesses since they too were accomplices to the crimes of which Wilde was accused.

The trial opened on 3 April 1895 amid scenes of near hysteria both in the press and the public galleries. The extent of the evidence massed against Wilde forced him to declare meekly, "I am the prosecutor in this case". Wilde's lawyer, Sir Edward George Clarke, opened the case by pre-emptively asking Wilde about two suggestive letters Wilde had written to Douglas, which the defence had in its possession. He characterised the first as a "prose sonnet" and admitted that the "poetical language" might seem strange to the court but claimed its intent was innocent. Wilde stated that the letters had been obtained by blackmailers who had attempted to extort money from him, but he had refused, suggesting they should take the £60 (equal to £6,800 today) offered, "unusual for a prose piece of that length". He claimed to regard the letters as works of art rather than something of which to be ashamed.

Carson, a fellow Dubliner who had attended Trinity College, Dublin at the same time as Wilde, cross-examined Wilde on how he perceived the moral content of his works. Wilde replied with characteristic wit and flippancy, claiming that works of art are not capable of being moral or immoral but only well or poorly made, and that only "brutes and illiterates", whose views on art "are incalculably stupid", would make such judgements about art. Carson, a leading barrister, diverged from the normal practice of asking closed questions. Carson pressed Wilde on each topic from every angle, squeezing out nuances of meaning from Wilde's answers, removing them from their aesthetic context and portraying Wilde as evasive and decadent. While Wilde won the most laughs from the court, Carson scored the most legal points. To undermine Wilde's credibility, and to justify Queensberry's description of Wilde as a "posing somdomite", Carson drew from the witness an admission of his capacity for "posing", by demonstrating that he had lied about his age on oath. Playing on this, he returned to the topic throughout his cross-examination. Carson also tried to justify Queensberry's characterization by quoting from Wilde's novel, The Picture of Dorian Gray, referring in particular to a scene in the second chapter, in which Lord Henry Wotton explains his decadent philosophy to Dorian, an "innocent young man", in Carson's words.

Carson then moved to the factual evidence and questioned Wilde about his friendships with younger, lower-class men. Wilde admitted being on a first-name basis and lavishing gifts upon them, but insisted that nothing untoward had occurred and that the men were merely good friends of his. Carson repeatedly pointed out the unusual nature of these relationships and insinuated that the men were prostitutes. Wilde replied that he did not believe in social barriers, and simply enjoyed the society of young men. Then Carson asked Wilde directly whether he had ever kissed a certain servant boy, Wilde responded, "Oh, dear no. He was a particularly plain boy – unfortunately ugly – I pitied him for it." Carson pressed him on the answer, repeatedly asking why the boy's ugliness was relevant. Wilde hesitated, then for the first time became flustered: "You sting me and insult me and try to unnerve me; and at times one says things flippantly when one ought to speak more seriously."

In his opening speech for the defence, Carson announced that he had located several male prostitutes who were to testify that they had had sex with Wilde. On the advice of his lawyers, Wilde dropped the prosecution. Queensberry was found not guilty, as the court declared that his accusation that Wilde was "posing as a Somdomite " was justified, "true in substance and in fact". Under the Libel Act 1843, Queensberry's acquittal rendered Wilde legally liable for the considerable expenses Queensberry had incurred in his defence, which left Wilde bankrupt.

Regina v. Wilde

After Wilde left the court, a warrant for his arrest was applied for on charges of sodomy and gross indecency. Robbie Ross found Wilde at the Cadogan Hotel, Pont Street, Knightsbridge, with Reginald Turner; both men advised Wilde to go at once to Dover and try to get a boat to France; his mother advised him to stay and fight. Wilde, lapsing into inaction, could only say, "The train has gone. It's too late." On 6 April 1895, Wilde was arrested for "gross indecency" under Section 11 of the Criminal Law Amendment Act 1885, a term meaning homosexual acts not amounting to buggery (an offence under a separate statute). At Wilde's instruction, Ross and Wilde's butler forced their way into the bedroom and library of 16 Tite Street, packing some personal effects, manuscripts, and letters. Wilde was then imprisoned on remand at Holloway where he received daily visits from Douglas.

Events moved quickly and his prosecution opened on 26 April 1895, before Mr Justice Charles. Wilde pleaded not guilty. He had already begged Douglas to leave London for Paris, but Douglas complained bitterly, even wanting to give evidence; he was pressed to go and soon fled to the Hotel du Monde. Fearing persecution, Ross and many others also left the United Kingdom during this time. Under cross examination Wilde was at first hesitant, then spoke eloquently:

Charles Gill (prosecuting): What is "the love that dare not speak its name"?

Wilde: "The love that dare not speak its name" in this century is such a great affection of an elder for a younger man as there was between David and Jonathan, such as Plato made the very basis of his philosophy, and such as you find in the sonnets of Michelangelo and Shakespeare. It is that deep spiritual affection that is as pure as it is perfect. It dictates and pervades great works of art, like those of Shakespeare and Michelangelo, and those two letters of mine, such as they are. It is in this century misunderstood, so much misunderstood that it may be described as "the love that dare not speak its name", and on that account of it I am placed where I am now. It is beautiful, it is fine, it is the noblest form of affection. There is nothing unnatural about it. It is intellectual, and it repeatedly exists between an older and a younger man, when the older man has intellect, and the younger man has all the joy, hope and glamour of life before him. That it should be so, the world does not understand. The world mocks at it, and sometimes puts one in the pillory for it.

This response was counter-productive in a legal sense as it only served to reinforce the charges of homosexual behaviour.

The trial ended with the jury unable to reach a verdict. Wilde's counsel, Sir Edward Clarke, was finally able to get a magistrate to allow Wilde and his friends to post bail. The Reverend Stewart Headlam put up most of the £5,000 surety required by the court, having disagreed with Wilde's treatment by the press and the courts. Wilde was freed from Holloway and, shunning attention, went into hiding at the house of Ernest and Ada Leverson, two of his firm friends. Edward Carson approached Frank Lockwood QC, the Solicitor General and asked "Can we not let up on the fellow now?" Lockwood answered that he would like to do so, but feared that the case had become too politicised to be dropped.

The final trial was presided over by Mr Justice Wills. On 25 May 1895 Wilde and Alfred Taylor were convicted of gross indecency and sentenced to two years' hard labour. The judge described the sentence, the maximum allowed, as "totally inadequate for a case such as this", and that the case was "the worst case I have ever tried". Wilde's response "And I? May I say nothing, my Lord?" was drowned out in cries of "Shame" in the courtroom.

Imprisonment

When first I was put into prison some people advised me to try and forget who I was. It was ruinous advice. It is only by realising what I am that I have found comfort of any kind. Now I am advised by others to try on my release to forget that I have ever been in a prison at all. I know that would be equally fatal. It would mean that I would always be haunted by an intolerable sense of disgrace, and that those things that are meant for me as much as for anybody else – the beauty of the sun and moon, the pageant of the seasons, the music of daybreak and the silence of great nights, the rain falling through the leaves, or the dew creeping over the grass and making it silver – would all be tainted for me, and lose their healing power, and their power of communicating joy. To regret one's own experiences is to arrest one's own development. To deny one's own experiences is to put a lie into the lips of one's own life. It is no less than a denial of the soul.

De Profundis

Wilde was incarcerated from 25 May 1895 to 18 May 1897.

He first entered Newgate Prison in London for processing, then was moved to Pentonville Prison, where the "hard labour" to which he had been sentenced consisted of many hours of walking a treadmill and picking oakum (separating the fibres in scraps of old navy ropes), and where prisoners were allowed to read only the Bible and The Pilgrim's Progress.

A few months later he was moved to Wandsworth Prison in London. Inmates there also followed the regimen of "hard labour, hard fare and a hard bed", which wore harshly on Wilde's delicate health. In November he collapsed during chapel from illness and hunger. His right ear drum was ruptured in the fall, an injury that later contributed to his death. He spent two months in the infirmary.

Richard B. Haldane, the Liberal MP and reformer, visited Wilde and had him transferred in November to Reading Gaol, 30 miles (48 km) west of London on 23 November 1895. The transfer itself was the lowest point of his incarceration, as a crowd jeered and spat at him on the railway platform. He spent the remainder of his sentence there, addressed and identified only as "C33" – the occupant of the third cell on the third floor of C ward.

About five months after Wilde arrived at Reading Gaol, Charles Thomas Wooldridge, a trooper in the Royal Horse Guards, was brought to Reading to await his trial for murdering his wife on 29 March 1896; on 17 June Wooldridge was sentenced to death and returned to Reading for his execution, which took place on Tuesday, 7 July 1896 – the first hanging at Reading in 18 years. From Wooldridge's hanging, Wilde later wrote The Ballad of Reading Gaol.

Wilde was not, at first, even allowed paper and pen but Haldane eventually succeeded in allowing access to books and writing materials. Wilde requested, among others: the Bible in French; Italian and German grammars; some Ancient Greek texts, Dante's Divine Comedy, Joris-Karl Huysmans's new French novel about Christian redemption En route, and essays by St Augustine, Cardinal Newman and Walter Pater.

Between January and March 1897 Wilde wrote a 50,000-word letter to Douglas. He was not allowed to send it, but was permitted to take it with him when released from prison. In reflective mode, Wilde coldly examines his career to date, how he had been a colourful agent provocateur in Victorian society, his art, like his paradoxes, seeking to subvert as well as sparkle. His own estimation of himself was: one who "stood in symbolic relations to the art and culture of my age". It was from these heights that his life with Douglas began, and Wilde examines that particularly closely, repudiating him for what Wilde finally sees as his arrogance and vanity: he had not forgotten Douglas' remark, when he was ill, "When you are not on your pedestal you are not interesting." Wilde blamed himself, though, for the ethical degradation of character that he allowed Douglas to bring about in him and took responsibility for his own fall, "I am here for having tried to put your father in prison." The first half concludes with Wilde forgiving Douglas, for his own sake as much as Douglas's. The second half of the letter traces Wilde's spiritual journey of redemption and fulfilment through his prison reading. He realised that his ordeal had filled his soul with the fruit of experience, however bitter it tasted at the time.

... I wanted to eat of the fruit of all the trees in the garden of the world ... And so, indeed, I went out, and so I lived. My only mistake was that I confined myself so exclusively to the trees of what seemed to me the sun-lit side of the garden, and shunned the other side for its shadow and its gloom.

Wilde was released from prison on 19 May 1897 and sailed that evening for Dieppe, France. He never returned to the UK.

On his release, he gave the manuscript to Ross, who may or may not have carried out Wilde's instructions to send a copy to Douglas (who later denied having received it). The letter was partially published in 1905 as De Profundis; its complete and correct publication first occurred in 1962 in The Letters of Oscar Wilde.

Decline: 1897–1900

Exile

Though Wilde's health had suffered greatly from the harshness and diet of prison, he had a feeling of spiritual renewal. He immediately wrote to the

86

Society of Jesus requesting a six-month Catholic retreat; when the request was denied, Wilde wept. "I intend to be received into the Catholic Church before long", Wilde told a journalist who asked about his religious intentions.

He spent his last three years impoverished and in exile. He took the name "Sebastian Melmoth", after Saint Sebastian and the titular character of Melmoth the Wanderer (a Gothic novel by Charles Maturin, Wilde's great-uncle). Wilde wrote two long letters to the editor of the Daily Chronicle, describing the brutal conditions of English prisons and advocating penal reform. His discussion of the dismissal of Warder Martin for giving biscuits to an anaemic child prisoner, repeated the themes of the corruption and degeneration of punishment that he had earlier outlined in The Soul of Man under Socialism.

Wilde spent mid-1897 with Robert Ross in the seaside village of Berneval-le-Grand in northern France, where he wrote The Ballad of Reading Gaol, narrating the execution of Charles Thomas Wooldridge, who murdered his wife in a rage at her infidelity. It moves from an objective story-telling to symbolic identification with the prisoners. No attempt is made to assess the justice of the laws which convicted them but rather the poem highlights the brutalisation of the punishment that all convicts share. Wilde juxtaposes the executed man and himself with the line "Yet each man kills the thing he loves". Wilde too was separated from his wife and sons. He adopted the proletarian ballad form and the author was credited as "C33", Wilde's cell number in Reading Gaol. He suggested that it be published in Reynolds' Magazine, "because it circulates widely among the criminal classes – to which I now belong – for once I will be read by my peers – a new experience for me". It was an immediate roaring commercial success, going through seven editions in less than two years, only after which "[Oscar Wilde]" was added to the title page, though many in literary circles had known Wilde to be the author. It brought him a small amount of money.

Although Douglas had been the cause of his misfortunes, he and Wilde were reunited in August 1897 at Rouen. This meeting was disapproved of by the friends and families of both men. Constance Wilde was already refusing to meet Wilde or allow him to see their sons, though she sent him money

– a meagre three pounds a week. During the latter part of 1897, Wilde and Douglas lived together near Naples for a few months until they were separated by their families under the threat of cutting off all funds.

Wilde's final address was at the dingy Hôtel d'Alsace (now known as L'Hôtel), on rue des Beaux-Arts in Saint-Germain-des-Prés, Paris. "This poverty really breaks one's heart: it is so sale [filthy], so utterly depressing, so hopeless. Pray do what you can" he wrote to his publisher. He corrected and published An Ideal Husband and The Importance of Being Earnest, the proofs of which, according to Ellmann, show a man "very much in command of himself and of the play" but he refused to write anything else: "I can write, but have lost the joy of writing".

He wandered the boulevards alone and spent what little money he had on alcohol. A series of embarrassing encounters with English visitors, or Frenchmen he had known in better days, drowned his spirit. Soon Wilde was sufficiently confined to his hotel to joke, on one of his final trips outside, "My wallpaper and I are fighting a duel to the death. One of us has got to go". On 12 October 1900 he sent a telegram to Ross: "Terribly weak. Please come". His moods fluctuated; Max Beerbohm relates how their mutual friend Reginald 'Reggie' Turner had found Wilde very depressed after a nightmare. "I dreamt that I had died, and was supping with the dead!" "I am sure", Turner replied, "that you must have been the life and soul of the party." Turner was one of the few of the old circle who remained with Wilde to the end and was at his bedside when he died.

Death

By 25 November 1900 Wilde had developed meningitis, then called cerebral meningitis. Robbie Ross arrived on 29 November, sent for a priest and Wilde was conditionally baptised into the Catholic Church by Fr Cuthbert Dunne, a Passionist priest from Dublin, Wilde having been baptised in the Church of Ireland and having moreover a recollection of Catholic baptism as a child, a fact later attested to by the minister of the sacrament, Fr Lawrence Fox. Fr Dunne recorded the baptism,

As the voiture rolled through the dark streets that wintry night, the sad story of Oscar Wilde was in part repeated to me... Robert Ross knelt by the bedside, assisting me as best he could while I administered conditional baptism, and afterwards answering the responses while I gave Extreme Unction to the prostrate man and recited the prayers for the dying. As the man was in a semi-comatose condition, I did not venture to administer the Holy Viaticum; still I must add that he could be roused and was roused from this state in my presence. When roused, he gave signs of being inwardly conscious... Indeed I was fully satisfied that he understood me when told that I was about to receive him into the Catholic Church and gave him the Last Sacraments... And when I repeated close to his ear the Holy Names, the Acts of Contrition, Faith, Hope and Charity, with acts of humble resignation to the Will of God, he tried all through to say the words after me.

Wilde died of meningitis on 30 November 1900. Different opinions are given as to the cause of the disease: Richard Ellmann claimed it was syphilitic; Merlin Holland, Wilde's grandson, thought this to be a misconception, noting that Wilde's meningitis followed a surgical intervention, perhaps a mastoidectomy; Wilde's physicians, Dr Paul Cleiss and A'Court Tucker, reported that the condition stemmed from an old suppuration of the right ear (from the prison injury, see above) treated for several years (une ancienne suppuration de l'oreille droite d'ailleurs en traitement depuis plusieurs années) and made no allusion to syphilis.

Burial

Wilde was initially buried in the Cimetière de Bagneux outside Paris; in 1909 his remains were disinterred and transferred to Père Lachaise Cemetery, inside the city. His tomb there was designed by Sir Jacob Epstein. It was commissioned by Robert Ross, who asked for a small compartment to be made for his own ashes, which were duly transferred in 1950. The modernist angel depicted as a relief on the tomb was originally complete with male genitalia, which were initially censored by French Authorities with a golden leaf. The genitals have since been vandalised; their current whereabouts are unknown. In 2000, Leon Johnson, a multimedia artist, installed a silver prosthesis to replace them. In 2011, the tomb was cleaned of the many lipstick marks left there by admirers and a glass barrier was installed to prevent further marks or damage.

The epitaph is a verse from The Ballad of Reading Gaol,

And alien tears will fill for him

Pity's long-broken urn,

For his mourners will be outcast men,

And outcasts always mourn.

Posthumous pardon

In 2017, Wilde was among an estimated 50,000 men who were pardoned for homosexual acts that were no longer considered offences under the Policing and Crime Act 2017. The Act is known informally as the Alan Turing law.

Biographies

Wilde's life has been the subject of numerous biographies since his death. The earliest were memoirs by those who knew him: often they are personal or impressionistic accounts which can be good character sketches, but are sometimes factually unreliable. Frank Harris, his friend and editor, wrote a biography, Oscar Wilde: His Life and Confessions (1916); though prone to exaggeration and sometimes factually inaccurate, it offers a good literary portrait of Wilde. Lord Alfred Douglas wrote two books about his relationship with Wilde. Oscar Wilde and Myself (1914), largely ghost-written by T. W. H. Crosland, vindictively reacted to Douglas's discovery that De Profundis was addressed to him and defensively tried to distance him from Wilde's scandalous reputation. Both authors later regretted their work. Later, in Oscar Wilde: A Summing Up (1939) and his Autobiography he was more sympathetic to Wilde. Of Wilde's other close friends, Robert Sherard; Robert Ross, his literary executor; and Charles Ricketts variously published biographies, reminiscences or correspondence. The first more or less objective biography of Wilde came about when Hesketh Pearson wrote Oscar Wilde: His Life and Wit (1946). In 1954 Wilde's son Vyvyan Holland published his memoir Son of Oscar Wilde, which recounts the difficulties Wilde's wife and children faced after his imprisonment. It was revised and updated by Merlin Holland in 1989.

Oscar Wilde, a critical study by Arthur Ransome was published in 1912. The book only briefly mentioned Wilde's life, but subsequently Ransome (and The Times Book Club) were sued for libel by Lord Alfred Douglas. In April 1913 Douglas lost the libel action after a reading of De Profundis refuted his claims.

Richard Ellmann wrote his 1987 biography Oscar Wilde, for which he posthumously won a National (USA) Book Critics Circle Award in 1988 and a Pulitzer Prize in 1989. The book was the basis for the 1997 film Wilde, directed by Brian Gilbert and starring Stephen Fry as the title character.

Neil McKenna's 2003 biography, The Secret Life of Oscar Wilde, offers an exploration of Wilde's sexuality. Often speculative in nature, it was widely criticised for its pure conjecture and lack of scholarly rigour. Thomas Wright's Oscar's Books (2008) explores Wilde's reading from his childhood in Dublin to his death in Paris. After tracking down many books that once belonged to Wilde's Tite Street library (dispersed at the time of his trials), Wright was the first to examine Wilde's marginalia.

Later on, I think everyone will recognise his achievements; his plays and essays will endure. Of course, you may think with others that his personality and conversation were far more wonderful than anything he wrote, so that his written works give only a pale reflection of his power. Perhaps that is so, and of course, it will be impossible to reproduce what is gone forever.

Robert Ross, 23 December 1900

In 2018, Matthew Sturgis' "Oscar: A Life," was published in London. The book incorporates rediscovered letters and other documents and is the most extensively researched biography of Wilde to appear since 1988.

Parisian literati, also produced several biographies and monographs on him. André Gide wrote In Memoriam, Oscar Wilde and Wilde also features in his journals. Thomas Louis, who had earlier translated books on Wilde into French, produced his own L'esprit d'Oscar Wilde in 1920. Modern books include Philippe Jullian's Oscar Wilde, and L'affaire Oscar Wilde, ou, Du danger de laisser la justice mettre le nez dans nos draps (The Oscar Wilde Affair, or, On the Danger of Allowing Justice to put its Nose in our Sheets) by Odon Vallet, a French religious historian. (Source: Wikipedia)